Where the Wild Winds Blow

The Whittlesey Wordsmiths

This anthology was lovingly put together by the Whittlesey
Wordsmiths, a U3A Creative Writing group.
The U3A (University of the Third Age) is an organisation for people no
longer in full-time employment; you can find your local UK branch at
https://www.u3a.org.uk/. Outside the UK, try
http://www.worldu3a.org/resources/

If you enjoy our work, please leave a review on Amazon.
Alternatively, contact us direct at whittleseywordsmiths@gmail.com
or through our blog at https://whittleseywordsmiths.com

Disclaimer
Apart from factual pieces, and where historical characters are
mentioned, stories and poems in this collection are works of fiction.
The names and characters in them are the invention of the writer.

Any resemblance to actual persons, living or dead, is coincidental,
whatever our relatives might claim.

CONTENTS

BEGIN AT THE BEGINNING

MIX 'n' MATCH CHARACTERS

ALMOST FAMILIAR

SETTING THE SCENE

PUNCHLINES

BEACHES

BITS AND PIECES

BEGIN AT THE END

FRAGMENTS

THE WHITTLESEY WORDSMITHS

BEGIN AT THE BEGINNING

First lines chosen from a selection.

Thanks to *The First Line* Literary Journal for inspiration and some of our first lines.
http://www.thefirstline.com/

Another Day

Val Chapman

The window was open just enough to let in the cool night air.

She was grateful for the breeze brushing her hot cheeks as she scanned the street below.

Turning to check the lock on the door behind her, she tried to slow her breathing, and thereby calm her heartbeat.

She'd had practice.

Over the last few months though, the outbursts and subsequent abuse had been getting more frequent, and her 'happy place' was getting further and further away.

She could still hear him downstairs – could hear the plates, and the pretty blue and white mugs she had picked up from the market, as they hit the floor.

He had said it was her fault.

It was always her fault.

He had said that if she served up 'that muck' again there would be 'hell to pay'.

Well, welcome to hell.

She didn't remember him saying that about the shepherd's pie, but it was the kind of thing he would say.

It was becoming quieter downstairs. With a resigned sigh she realised it was probably because there was nothing left for him to smash. She would normally have put the plates and things away before he came home, but she had been cleaning the kitchen cupboards and time had gotten the better of her.

She could usually tell the kind of night that lay ahead depending on whether or not she could smell him as he came in the room. Tonight though, had taken her by surprise. Tonight it seemed that alcohol was not the catalyst.

Tonight it appeared to be 'just her'.

She leant forward and rested her forehead on the bathroom window. How had it come to this?

It had been a whirlwind romance. Brought up in a children's home, she had been bowled over by this kind, funny man who made her feel like a princess, and a sexy one at that. All his friends said so. They used to buy her things – well, drinks mostly... but it didn't matter what they said, or did to her, she knew they were just meant for each other.

He'd said so.

As time wore on, he became more possessive – locking her in the house when he went out, only letting her out to go shopping while he waited in the car.

She knew, though, that he was doing this for her own good, so she didn't mind too much at first. The world was becoming a far worse place, he'd said, with too many bad people in it, and he would do whatever it took to protect her. It was dealing with so many 'bad people' that put him in these terrible moods, and he took it out on her. But, as he pointed out, he went easy on her because he loved her. Anyone else wouldn't be so kind.

And in his way, he was kind.

After all, he'd bought her a kitten to keep her company, and she hadn't even had to ask. He could tell she was upset when their last cat, Susie, had died. The little fluffy creature had been a delight, snuggling into her neck during their long days together. It was after one of his rages that poor Susie had died.

She had managed to calm him down enough to run away into the bathroom, but he wasn't quite calm enough. When things had settled and she had gone back downstairs, Susie was lying dead on the kitchen floor.

He had said that she just lay down and died. But she wasn't so sure.

They had buried her in a corner of their tiny garden, and he had comforted her while they stood, heads bowed, over the little mound of earth.

See, he did still care. He was still kind. Wasn't he?

He had come home a few weeks later with a beautiful grey kitten for her. He knew how much she missed Susie and he'd wanted to make her feel better.

Together they named her Millie, and she had turned out to be every bit as good at cuddles as Susie was.

He'd found a new job, and things between them were a little calmer. For a while.

It was her fault, of course. She should never have looked at the delivery man like that.

Or worn that t-shirt.

Or bought a different brand of coffee.

He wasn't as remorseful as he used to be.

In the beginning, he would cry with her, tell her how sorry he was, promise he wouldn't do it again.

Then, when he'd made her realise it was her fault, she was the one saying 'sorry', and promising not to do it again.

A few months ago at the market, someone had noticed.

He hadn't been watching her – too busy chatting to some bloke. If he had looked across, all he would have seen was some woman talking to her. She wasn't talking back, so she might have gotten away with it.

Turned out this woman recognised something in her. She'd 'been there'apparently and wanted to help.

Every week since, this woman had approached her, giving her leaflets with phone numbers on, and gently encouraging her. This one woman had made her feel something she hadn't felt for a long time.

It might have been self-respect.

It might have been bravery.

It might have been just 'human'.

But whatever it was, it was making her stronger. It was helping her to raise her eyes from the floor and look around her.

A gentle miaowing brought her back. Millie nuzzled her legs. She had vowed she wouldn't let this kitten suffer the way Susie must have.

Holding her breath, she bent, slowly eased the bath panel away from the bath and felt behind it. The bag she had packed was still there and gave her some comfort. When the time was right, she would go. It was getting close, she felt. For now, she stood, looked out of the window and checked on her escape route.

Taking a deep breath of the cool night air, she picked up her kitten, and unlocked the bathroom door.

~~~

I Wanted You to be the First to Know

Wendy Fletcher

'I wanted you to be the first to know,' Rowan tentatively confided in me.

I hugged her tight against me and fought back the tears of relief that threatened to drown both of us.

I wanted to tell her how much I loved her and how worried I had been but she was a teenager and I knew she would call me a silly old softy so I sniffed back the tears and gasped, 'Let's have another coffee to celebrate.'

We were in the café at Piccadilly Station and crowds milled around us but we had managed to find a table by the far wall which afforded us a little privacy. I had arrived early and let my first coffee go cold, untouched, as I tried to prepare for Rowan's arrival.

What would I say to her? How would I broach the subject? Should I mention her mother's illness or would that be too tactless? How do you say to a nineteen-year-old, 'I'm frightened for you'?

Now she was here and all the anguish of the past few weeks had melted away in laughter.

This whole fiasco had started to unfold in February when I received the first letter from Rowan. She was a student now, studying English at a top London university and I was so proud of her. She had not had an easy start in life. She was my favourite niece, the only child of my elder sister, Poppy.

During her early years, she had spent a lot of time with me as Poppy fought her demons. Sometimes Rowan was dropped off at our house in the middle of the night because her mother had been admitted to hospital again, deluded and paranoid.

As a child, Poppy had shown no signs of what was to come but, at the age of nineteen, she suddenly changed into a different person; introverted, obsessive, haunted by images of monsters and vampires and ghouls.

She responded to treatment and became well enough to marry and have Rowan but had never fully recovered and the relapses went on throughout Rowan's childhood.

It had been difficult to maintain regular contact as she was prone to outbursts of accusation, and would shut herself away for long periods, convinced that the family were her enemies.

In later years, I had faced the reality that she was never going to be completely cured and tried not to think of all we had shared as children: two sisters close in age, growing up in a family of boys. Mostly, the memories were painful and I shut them away, consoling myself with the knowledge that I would always be there if she decided she needed me.

Meantime I had focussed on helping Rowan when she struggled with feelings of rejection as a small child, then a desperate need to put things right as she hit the phase where children blame themselves for everything and, most recently, in coming to terms with the reality that there is really little she can do.

Then came the letter, post-marked February 20th. I opened it quickly, always pleased to get an amusing note from my niece about college life.

I clung to the kitchen dresser as the words danced before my eyes.

'I wanted you to be the first to know. The vampire swooped, blood already fresh on her lips.....'

I couldn't read on.

My worst nightmare had jumped out of that envelope. My beautiful, funny, talented niece was turning into her mother. I had pushed the fear that this might happen so far to the back of my mind that I had managed to celebrate her nineteenth birthday without ruining it with dread. This had been the crucial turning point for my sister.

Now there was no room for denial; I held the proof in my hands. I wanted to ring Rowan immediately but what would I have said?

Instead, I ripped the letter to shreds. I didn't want to read any more. Somehow, that would have made it more real.

I avoided looking in my post for the familiar scrawl that I had always welcomed and over the next three weeks I began to relax. Perhaps it had all been a nightmare, born of my fear now that Rowan had reached nineteen.

It was a Monday when the next envelope dropped through the letterbox. I made a mug of coffee before I opened it. I knew this was the decider. If this was a 'normal for a teenager' letter, then my imagination was the one that was running away. If it was weird in any way, I had to confront Rowan.

The envelope probably wasn't trickier than any other, but I fumbled and struggled to open it.

'I wanted you to be the first to know. When the shadows fall and I hear the beating of wings....'

I closed my eyes but only for a moment. I knew now what I had to do. I rang Rowan and didn't give her time to ask any questions; this was not something to be done in a phone call. I just said I needed to see her urgently, tomorrow at Piccadilly. I could work out the rest when I got there.

I had the second letter in my hand when Rowan joined me at the table. There was no point in skirting around the matter so I launched straight in.

'When I got your first letter, I was really worried, but now, with this second one....'

Rowan took it from me.

'This is the third one I sent,' she spoke quietly. 'Did you not get the first one that explained what I was doing?'

Suddenly there was a glimmer of hope. Could I have misunderstood something?

'Oh, Auntie Rose, I can see why you were worried. I can see how it looked.'

'It's about your mum,' I whispered.

'Yes, it is,' she nodded, 'but not in the way you're thinking. My first letter explained it all.

'Mum got in touch with me when I turned nineteen; she wanted to make sure I was all right. We got chatting. She has so much bottled up. She said it would make a good story. I said I was an English student and wanted to be a writer. We just got together and it all started coming out.

'I'm writing her autobiography and her therapist says it's a real breakthrough, just sharing her thoughts for the first time. He thinks it will make an excellent story, and I wanted you to be the first to know. Then, as I wrote you that first letter, I realised that I had the title for the book and each chapter will start with those words – "I wanted you to be the first to know".'

~~~

A Grubby Tale

Val Chapman

"I wanted you to be the first to know," Rowan tentatively confided in me. "I'm going to change. I don't feel right in this body, I need to do something."

I stopped eating and turned to look at him.

"Really? Why?

"When?

"How?"

It wasn't as though it was a total surprise. I could tell Rowan had been – shall we say – unsettled of late. Summer was just around the corner, and our little group of friends had been looking towards the future.

"I know you have been wondering," he pressed on. "I've been hearing rumours for a while now, so I thought I should just face it, and tell you first. After all, we've always been close, haven't we?"

This was undeniably true.

I, too, had heard various murmurings, but tried to push them to the back of my mind. We had been together for what seemed like forever, living close to one another and spending most of our days in each other's company. We were so alike, yet so different.

In fact I used to be jealous of Rowan, growing up. He was so athletic and strong, compared to weedy little me. And I would have given anything to have thick, dark hair like him. As time wore on, I realised that we were just two separate creatures, he and I. But our friendship was solid and total.

"Are you sure Rowan?" I asked. "Have you really thought this through?"

"It's not really something that I have a choice about – you know that. It's really more of a compulsion. I need to do this. I have to do this. I hope you won't be angry with me."

"Oh, I could never be angry with you, silly. You mean the world to me, you always will."

We spent time talking and walking until it was time to say goodbye, and Rowan left to go to the special place he had found, promising to come back when it was all over. It had been wonderful being with Rowan but now he had to fulfill his destiny.

It is a scary prospect for caterpillars like us to transform into a butterfly or moth and soon enough it would be my turn, but changing is something we all do when it is our time. Whenever Rowan came back, we would meet up again, friends re-united in all our new glory.

~~~

Van

Jan Cunningham

The transit turned onto the trunk road, heading away from the housing estate.

Well, where are we going now? Off to his mates, I'll bet. He does my head in. Accelerator, brake, accelerator, brake, what a way to drive. He has no consideration for my suspension or tyres. Why he's in such a hurry to get to heaven is beyond my comprehension.

Still anything's better than being stuck in his driveway, staring at the garage door all night. When his dad's at home there isn't room for two on the driveway so he leaves me in the residents' car park, next to a snazzy little red number. She's a cutie.

My driver is a plumber: young, flash, and thinks he's god's gift. The way he treats me is nigh-on criminal: hardly puts any petrol in – tight git. I'm gasping my last when he finally takes me to a petrol station.

And – talk about speed – he thinks he's Lewis Hamilton. He forgets I'm getting on a bit and it fair takes the fumes out of my exhaust.

It was all right at first; he just used me for work. Loaded up his gear and off we went to various jobs and, I have to give it to him, he's a hard worker.

Then he started racing. He and his mates would go up on the waste ground next to the old quarry; take turns racing their vans against each other and bet on the results. Well, that wasn't in my contract. I ask you, at my age. Some nights, by the time they're finished I wish I'd gone to the scrapyard.

Now, here's the thing: I overheard them talking the other night but I couldn't quite make out what it was about. I heard the word Derby, but that didn't mean anything to me... then.

The next thing I knows he's got a new van and I'm being shuffled off to his mates' workshop. I'm scared now as I don't trust those three idiots and they keep referring to a paper that appears to be instructions. For what, I'd like to know?

Well, I didn't have to wait long. Next evening after work, they started ripping out all my interior, then removing headlights, tail-lights, all the plastic, trim and lastly the glass.

What's going on?

I was naked as a new model on the assembly line. If I could have crossed my wheels, I would have. I was so embarrassed, but they didn't give a hoot – just kept reading out instructions and laughing.

Next they cut out my front and rear fenders – apparently to stop my tyres from getting cut. (Who's going to cut me?)

They cut a hole in my bonnet to allow easy access for putting out fires. (Who's going to set fire to me?) Then to crown it all they took off the driver's door, filled it with cement and put it back. This is to protect the driver from hits. (Who's going to hit him?) They think it's such a hoot, threatening to come back the night after to finish me off.

If he'd put any petrol in me, I would have done a runner I can tell you, but as he hadn't....

The three of them returned next evening, armed with paint, brushes, and cans of spray-paint.

Now what are they up to?

They painted my driver's door black with a large number three in white. This was apparently to identify the driver. Then an argument started as to what I would be called and which colours would be used. My choice would have been "Nutters", but they ignored me and settled on "Three Musketeers" with green and yellow for colours.

After they finished making me look a right prat, they sauntered off down to their local nearby for what they called "a well-earned bevvy", leaving me to ponder on what was coming next. And I wasn't looking forward to it whatever it was.

On Sunday morning, I'm driven onto a low-loader. What the hell is going to happen to me?

I haven't a clue as we bowl along the country roads, sun shining, blue sky and the smell of fresh-mown grass. Normally I would have enjoyed a run in the country but not today.

I'm scared.

Eventually we turn off onto a wide track and pull up next to a field. There are concrete blocks laid in a circle, making a wide ring with cars revving and roaring around the middle of this muddy patch. I watch the goings-on in horror.

They were skidding around, bashing and crashing into each other, engines smoking, car bumpers flying and even wheels coming off. The large crowd watching egged the drivers on, shouting encouragement and whooping with delight at the antics in the arena. The noise was deafening, and I could smell fumes from the vehicles mixed in with all the other smells: BBQ, hot dogs, beefburgers... nauseating.

Was this to be my end? After years of loyal service, am I to be bashed, crashed, skidded into, and torn apart just for the fun of it? If I'd had any screen wash left, I would have cried.

As the day wore on I began to hope, but then came the announcement I had been dreading.

"Now folks, the last event of the Demolition Derby is for vans. So would all the competitors line up in the ring."

So this was it. My end.

My driver put on his brand-new, fancy crash helmet and gloves, got in the cab, and off we went. We lined up in the ring with bonnets facing the crowd and rear ends to the middle.

"Ready? Five, Four, Three, Two, One. Crash and Bash!"

Every one drove backwards into the middle and rammed each other. Ouch! Oye! Mind out! But my cries were to no avail. OK, if this is my finale let's make it a goodun.

We pushed, shoved, rammed... sideways on, rear to rear, bonnet to bonnet. It seemed that the only rule was do-not-hit-the-driver's-side-full-on-deliberately – otherwise, go for it.

And we did. My driver was pumped-up: yelling and whooping, spinning me round, hurtling backwards and forwards. One van's engine caught fire, so we had to stop for a few minutes while it was dealt with. One down, five to go.

Then two vans clashed head on so badly they couldn't separate so that was them done for.

Three down, three to go.

By now, the noise from the crowd was deafening, smoke pouring out from the engines, dust swirling in clouds and enveloping the ring, making it difficult to see clearly.

My cocky young driver was having a ball. He drove me hard and fast, and although I was dented, battered, and nearly buggered, we still managed to skid, turn on a sixpence and get some decent rams in. But no-one left was going to roll over easily.

The battle was fierce.

Then the number 101 van, with Suky written on the side, shunted the other van so hard it finished up straddling the concrete barrier, rocking backwards and forwards, wheels spinning frantically but unable to get back on the track.

Four down. Just the two of us left.

I just wanted the whole miserable charade to end. Death by a thousand dents. My bodywork was crushed, wheels dented and wobbly, back and front bumpers hanging off, and bonnet knocked up.

I'd had enough. I was knackered.

Then Suky seemed to come out of nowhere and shunted me so hard I went into a wild spin.

But my driver wasn't taking that. He reversed quickly and hit Suki hard on the passenger side. The van went up and teetered, nearly going over, but just managing to right itself in time for our next belt.

This time we pushed Suki right tight to the concrete slabs. I was hoping that was it... but no. Suki managed to skitter away and drove to the far end of the arena.

My driver turned me to face the van. With both engines revving hard we set off.

If I'd had any eyes to close, they would have been shut tight as we hurtled towards each other. There was an almighty bang as we clashed bonnet to bonnet and both front ends went up into the air. For a split second, we must have looked like two boxing kangaroos: fronts in the air at a forty-five degree angle, wheels spinning and engines screamimg.

Then it was over. Suki went over backwards but we came down onto our front wheels.

We had won.

My driver was up on what was left of my bonnet; jumping up and down, fist punching the air. The crowd were clapping and cheering as he was crowned the winner and given a bottle of some cheap fizz to squirt over all and sundry.

Well, bully for us.

Thank God it's over. Right now, the scrap yard looks rather inviting. I mean, I've had a long career, not done too badly with drivers, and we've all go to go sometime – right?

Then I overheard my driver and his mates talking. It seems they are thinking of patching me up and doing it all again!

Noooooooooooooooooooooooooo....

~~~

Millie

Val Chapman

Millie was livid when she went back to the laboratory.

She pulled the door fiercely behind her, causing it to bang, which reverberated around the room. Her fellow pupils looked up.

"Millicent Mayhew, treat the place with some respect, and sit down."

"Sorry, sir," she mumbled as she pulled out a stool from underneath the bench.

The class, by now, was used to Millie's little outbursts. She had come to the school last term, and seemed to have a huge chip on her shoulder for some reason. Her classmates had no idea why the teachers tolerated her behaviour, but as far as they were concerned, she was just an angry twelve-year-old who wouldn't settle and didn't seem to want to make friends.

There was one boy in school she spent time with though. Lucas was a calm, quiet boy, quite different to Millie, which served to prove the point that opposites attract.

When Millie glanced up and saw Lucas, his shy smile seemed to settle her somehow, and she took out her book, ready to join in with the lesson.

As was the case with most of their experiments, Lucas excelled, with Millie being distinctly average. She was constantly told she had great potential, but time and again Millie felt she was letting everyone down by not being the star pupil she was supposed to be.

The sound of the bell indicated the end of the lesson and, relieved from their concentration, the class became noisy again.

"Come on, let's go to lunch," said Lucas, "then you can tell me what happened at the meeting with the Head."

In the dining hall, Millie and Lucas took their trays to the seat by the window in the far corner. It was their usual spot, and they were far enough away from everyone to make conversation comfortable.

"So," Lucas pressed, "what happened?"

"Well..." Millie sighed. "I tried to tell them I shouldn't be here, and should just go to an ordinary school, but they said that really wasn't an option any more. They went on about how they had taken the pressure off by changing my name, and all the indications were that it is just a matter of time before I 'come into my own'.

"And I do sometimes think that it might be true, but it's so hard to live up to." Millie pushed the remains of her lunch to one side. "So it looks like I'm stuck here after all.

"But at least no-one has picked up on your name being Grainger, although it's probably only a matter of time before someone twigs that my real name is Potter. We may be Harry and Hermione's long lost siblings, but it doesn't mean we can carry on where they left off."

"I think I'm more of a muggle than Hermione ever was," Lucas observed.

"Huh, you're doing great. I'm the muggle round here. I think wizardry has passed me by. Still, I suppose Hogwarts is a good school, so if anyone can train me, they can."

They cleared away their lunch trays, picked up their wands, and went to their next class.

~~~

Leo's Story

Tessa Thomson

Leo massaged the back of his neck, thankful the meeting was finally over. Those seated began to stand. They moved away. His hand felt damp, and small trickles of sweat were making their way down the inside of his shirt. For a moment, he was unable to move. He wasn't sure his legs could take his weight. Using the arms of the chair, he moved to stand, and immediately felt unable to carry out this simple manoeuvre.

"Are you alright?"

His hearing seemed blurred. A voice somewhere far away was talking, lips moving, but Leo, without thinking, just sunk back into the chair. "Yes, yes I'm fine."

The voice spoke again. "I know it's a shock. But we will have more information in due course."

What now? Where could he go? What should he do? There was no plan for this.

He stood to leave, a knot in his stomach forcing him to lean over as if in pain. He left the station and made his way to the car. His keys – where were his keys? He fumbled for them in his pockets, found them, dropped them to the floor, and almost followed them, head buzzing, down onto that stony path. He wanted to crawl away; he wanted the day to start again.

Start again. Thursday morning, started as usual, uneventful, nothing out of the ordinary.

Leo imagined that when they married, he would lie awake watching her sleep, peaceful and safe. He fantasised about watching her breathe, her breath in small puffs, making her lips slightly part, her chest rise and fall, her eyes slightly flicker.

He had no physical experience of her. Sally lived in France. Leo, born and raised in London, still lived in the house he had shared until recently with his mother.

Sally worked at the French end of the company and Leo, in London, was a very junior member of staff. Normally, their paths would not have crossed but – and Leo thought it was fate – orders from France had not been arriving at their correct destinations in England. Leo was tasked with finding why, and Sally was his contact in France.

At first he emailed her. To his surprise, her replies always seemed cheeky, almost flirty. He decided the problem required him to phone her directly. Her voice gave him goose-bumps. Yes, of course, the accent helped but somehow it was more than that. She laughed in a way that made him feel foolish. She had a hesitation in her voice that made her seem vulnerable even at a distance. She made him feel older and wiser somehow. But at the same time, he felt incredibly young.

He told himself a hundred times he was being stupid. He couldn't see her; she might be fifty for all he knew. He knew, from his love of film, that French women remained glamorous into old age and talked with husky, sexy voices. But he hoped she was young.

By now he had spoken to her a handful of times, trying all the while to find out a little more. He found excuses to call her, and their conversations became such that they could talk easily. Not just about work. He felt theirs was a romance blossoming over the wires and cables that ran under the sea.

Sally's mother was English; her father was from Sierra Leone. After they divorced, Sally's mother moved to France when Sally was three years old. Sally's mother was a dancer who had trained in London and was touring in Sierra Leone when she met Sally's father. It was not a happy union, and ended after only a few months, so Sally had never met her father. Her mother had passed away a few years ago.

He told her about some parts of his life. He tried not to talk about the sad bits that still caused him so much pain. He tried to make his life seem more interesting than it actually was. But with no family now, no pets, a fairly boring job and few interests, it was hard to make it sound other than what it was – very lonely. But somehow, they moved from this tentative start to a more solid footing, and arranged Sally's first visit to England. He hoped that, with time, he could share with her all that there was to know about his life before she became such a big part of it. He believed life would be so much better with her. At last he felt he could share all that he had been unable to share with anyone else.

He stood on the station platform waiting for the train to arrive. Her train was due at twelve-thirty but he had been there since nine o'clock. He was up at six, had dressed at least three times, and was already regretting the blazer, and blue jeans. The hideous tie was tucked out of sight in his pocket. He hoped their meeting would be like a scene from his favourite film, *Brief Encounter* – Sally walking toward him through a cloud of steam, and into his arms. He would hold her and kiss her cheek, and life for him would begin.

He looked again at the clock; it was twelve-thirty-one. There was no sign of the train. People on the platform were looking down the line, checking their watches. Minutes passed; they seemed like hours. But there was still no sign of the train.

Station staff appeared and moved along the platform. The station clock struck one and now passengers waiting to board for the return journey were asking questions. Station staff were clearly unprepared with answers. Mobile phones began ringing.

Then, quite suddenly, a man took Leo's arm. "Are you waiting for someone?" He nodded.

"Would you like to come with me?"

One or two other people joined them, and Leo's heart began to race. The young man took them to a small room where Leo was joined by an anxious older man and a young girl. They sat, as Leo stood by the window, his face drawn to the now empty platform. Some passengers had moved to another platform, some were taken to a different office. It was one-thirty now, and very quiet.

The older gentleman and the young girl were talking to each other. Leo heard the man say the train may have been late leaving Paris.

"Or maybe," Leo said, "leaves on the line." They smiled at this but inside Leo was not smiling.

A door in an inner office opened, another young man, wearing a railway uniform asked them to join him. They moved to another room in which two other people Leo recognised from the platform were already seated. They sat in a semicircle as if waiting to play musical chairs. The young railwayman had flushed red cheeks and, Leo noticed, hauntingly blue eyes that were watching the open door. An older man in a grey suit entered the room, so quietly that the group seemed as one to be startled by his arrival.

"Ladies and gentlemen, I am very sorry to have to tell you that there has been a serious incident with this morning's train from Paris. We are waiting for confirmation about what has happened, but I can say at this time that an explosion whilst the train was in a tunnel has caused considerable damage. I am not able to say any more just now, but if you could all come with me, I will need to take some details from you."

Leo wanted to ask questions but somehow couldn't speak. The young girl was crying and the older gentleman held her hand. The young man in the railway uniform led the way from the room. They followed like sheep along the corridor to another room where they sat along wooden tables as if attending an important meeting. Leo fully expected someone to take coffee orders.

Several uniformed people took details. Leo gave as much information as he could, realising that he actually knew very little about Sally, or her journey. People moved around him but Leo sat, cold and quite numb, all feeling gone from his legs and hands.

Was the life he had hoped for all these months drifting away? He tried to imagine what Sally might look like. What she would be wearing.

"Thank you all," said a voice from the end of the table.

~~~

Finders Keepers

Valerie Fish

As she trudged down the alley, Cenessa saw a small, bedraggled boy standing all alone; the poor thing was shivering all over. He couldn't have been more than three years old.

Where was his mother? She looked behind her to see if anyone was around, but there was nobody in sight in either direction.

'Hello, poppet, what's your name?'

'Mummy gone.'

He looked up at her with sorrowful eyes, a single tear rolling down his cheek.

Her heart melted.

'It's okay, little one, you can come home with me, I'll look after you.'

After a moment's hesitation, he took her outstretched hand. It was only a short walk back to her house over the stream and down the lane – not long enough for Cenessa to think about what she was doing.

Later, after she had given the boy a hot bath, she sat at the kitchen table watching him devour a jam sandwich and glass of milk, and wondered if she should be calling the police. She convinced herself that if his mother really cared about him, she wouldn't have left him to wander all alone and besides, she had so much love she could give him, so what was the problem?

The house seemed so empty since she'd lost Joshua. Her husband didn't really understand. She was the one that had carried him all those months, and all for nothing. At least Joe had his job to keep him occupied. For Cenessa, every day was the same and seemed to go on forever. He wouldn't let her go out to work. He held the old-fashioned belief that it was a woman's job to stay at home, spending all day keeping the house in order and having her husband's dinner ready, waiting for him when he got home.

Maybe this was meant to be; maybe God had sent this child for her. She knew he could never replace Joshua, but maybe it would go some way to filling the emptiness in her heart

She deserved some happiness.

The boy's eyes were beginning to droop. She took him in her arms and carried him upstairs and into the nursery. She laid him in the cot that they had never been able to take down.

Back downstairs with a cup of tea, Cenessa started to fret about how Joe would react when he came home to find a strange child in the house. She hoped he wouldn't be too cross. Hopefully, she would be able to talk him round and convince him what a difference this lovely little boy could make to their lives. The boy hadn't said a word since she'd brought him home. Later, when he woke up, she would try and at least get him to tell her his name. If not, maybe they could name him themselves. Isaac? Samuel? She was still thinking of names when Joe arrived home, looking exhausted after a hard day's graft. That didn't bode well. But she couldn't put off telling him. She hadn't heard a peep out of the child upstairs.

'Cenessa, are you crazy? He's not ours to keep; he belongs to someone else. His mother's probably out there now, frantically searching for him.'

'But we know everyone in the village; he doesn't belong to anyone round here. And she couldn't have cared that much about him could she?'

It was difficult to reason with her. Maybe he could have chosen his words more carefully; calling her crazy was rather cruel. He hadn't meant to hurt her. He knew she'd not been right ever since Joshua, although it was something they never talked about.

'At least come upstairs and see the wee mite. You'll love him, Joe. He's adorable.'

Grudgingly he followed her up into Joshua's room; he tried to avoid going there if at all possible.

The cot was empty.

Cenessa screamed.

'He's gone, he's gone!'

She began crying hysterically. 'We must go and find him, anything could happen to him.'

'Calm down Cenessa, you're being ridiculous.'

'You don't believe me. I'm telling you, he was here!'

Eventually she wore herself out.

'I think you should call the doctor's tomorrow and get an appointment. Maybe he can adjust your pills.'

'I don't want pills. I just want my baby back.'

Not knowing what he could say that would make things any better, he said nothing.

'I'm going to bed. I think you should sleep in the spare room tonight. I need to be on my own.'

The atmosphere at breakfast next morning was somewhat strained, with Cenessa still upset and angry with him for not believing her, and Joe thinking whatever he said would have no effect. He left for work without a word spoken between them, hoping that by the time he came home in the evening she would have seen sense. Otherwise, he would have to persuade her that she needed to see 'somebody'.

But Cenessa knew it wasn't her imagination or simply a bad dream; she had found that poor little boy and brought him home. And now he could be anywhere, lost and all alone just like yesterday. She had to go out and look for him.

Arriving at the village green, she saw two familiar faces deep in conversation; it was a favourite spot for village gossip. As she approached them, she heard the words, 'It's just so sad, the poor wee mite.'

'Have you found him, have you found my little boy?'

The two women exchanged glances.

'Your little boy, Cenessa? What do you mean, you haven't...' one of them started, but stopped mid-sentence. 'We were talking about that tragic accident yesterday.'

Cenessa's blood ran cold.

'What accident?' But she knew.

'A woman and her child, up on the lane. She lost control of her car, overturned and rolled down the bank into the river. Not from round here. They were visiting relatives; she wouldn't have been familiar with the road – probably going too fast. Both of them killed instantly, if that's any blessing. Miraculously there wasn't a mark on the child.

'He couldn't have been more than three years old.'

~~~

The Alien

Caroline Cowan

"I wanted you to be the first to know," Rowan tentatively confided in me.

"OK Row, what's the problem?"

At twenty-two Rowan and I had always been friends. We had watched each other's backs, right through school, even celebrating our eighteenth birthdays together. I had been there for him, after his mother died suddenly when he was fourteen. He was an only child, so now it was just him and his father who spent most of his time at work.

Rowan and I enjoyed going out on our motorbikes. We would pack our rucksacks and go off for weekends to the coast just to get away from the hustle and bustle of life. I finished college and went to work as a designer, and Rowan went to work in IT. We often dated girls as a foursome but felt too young to settle down and start thinking of a family.

"I don't know where to start," said Rowan, "but here's the problem. I have special powers and I'm frightened to use them. You are the only person I have ever told and because I know you so well, Jay, and you have been my friend for so long, I trust you not to say anything to anyone. Even my father doesn't know. If people were to find out, I would be-seen as a freak."

I collapsed with laughter, which didn't help Rowan feel any better.

"Sorry, Row. Go on, tell me the rest."

"I will if you stay quiet while I'm telling you."

I made a zipper motion over my mouth.

"It all started when I turned eighteen. At first I didn't know what was happening so I ignored it. I thought it was just part of growing up. A kid up the road was hit by a ball and it knocked him out. As I was passing, something drove me to put my hand on his head.

He woke up and it was as though nothing had happened to him. I kept looking at my hands as though I would see something but there was nothing there. I kept on walking.

"You know what kids are like, they just accepted it and got on with their game.

"What do you think Jay? Do you think I'm going mad?"

"Ooh cool! I don't think you are going mad, Row, or imagining it. Perhaps you should see a vicar or someone about it if that would make you feel better. So is that it? No sparks come out of you, or you make yourself invisible? Lots of people have healing hands so you aren't on your own."

"Yes, I think maybe it's healing hands. I don't really know as I've tried to ignore the powers, but I do feel them building up inside me. I feel I can only use them for good but don't know the consequences if I tried other things. Not that I want to.

"I somehow feel my mother had them as well and she, too, kept them a secret. If I think back, there were some strange happenings in the house. I never seemed to be ill."

"I won't tell anyone Row. You can trust me."

We loved the countryside – riding through the valleys above deep ravines. Neither of us had ever been "one of the lads"; we had a healthy respect for cars and lorries. We would take in the beautiful surroundings, often stopping at one of the pubs en route, sometimes leaving our bikes to walk instead.

We probably came over as "boring" to some of our friends but didn't care. We admired breath-taking views, and would sit and watch the sun going down before heading back to our bikes and riding off to our bed and breakfast.

It was on one of these trips that Rowan confided in me. The morning after, we set off on the next leg of our journey to the coast. Whilst riding past one of the deep ravines we noticed a broken tree and skid marks on the road. We stopped our bikes to peer over the steep sides.

"There's a car down there. I can just see it," said Rowan. "The people in it must be badly hurt, falling that far. I don't think it was long ago, but I can't see any movement."

"Better phone for help; we can't get down there. They will need ropes to get to them."

I was beginning to panic but Rowan was calmly stepping to the edge and spreading out his arms. There was a faint glow round him.

I exclaimed, "You can fly?" as he glided over the edge.

I watched in amazement as he landed at the bottom. The distance made it difficult to see what he was doing. Then I saw him carry two elderly people up from the car and lie them down at the top.

He held their hands. The couple regained consciousness and sat up, looking around them. They were perfectly OK. Rowan had completely healed them.

The emergency vehicles arrived and took them both to hospital to be checked over, even though they had no perceivable injuries.

Rowan was unfazed by it all.

At the end of an eventful weekend, we rode home as if nothing had happened.

"How are you, Rowan, after saving that couple?" I asked. "You *flew*, carried two people to safety, healed them. You didn't even seem surprised.

"I was fine, Jay, I had help. Someone was talking me through it all. I think it was my mother."

"I didn't see anyone else around," I said.

"No there wasn't anyone else around, it was in my mind. She told me to stretch out my arms and let myself go. Then she told me I had the strength to carry both people back up to safety. It was wonderful, knowing she was there."

"I thought your mother had died."

"So did I, Jay. Well, that's what I was told. When you are a child, you accept everything without question; now I'm not so sure.

"Last night I had a visit from my mother. She materialised in my room and woke me up. I wasn't frightened – just a little surprised. She told me she wasn't from this planet but from a tiny planet way beyond the stars called Kingston – well, that's what it translates to. My father is also from there but it isn't his time to return. My mother was ill, so had to go back to be healed and to stay well. We do catch Earth's illnesses. They were both sent to Earth to study the way Earthlings live. That's why everything had to be so secret.

"It was wonderful, Jay. I was so thrilled to see her. Apparently, she often visits my father but I wasn't ready to know until now. After saving that couple, she knew it was time to tell me everything. In a short while, it will be my time to return to Kingston and be with my own people but until then I am here to live like a human.

"What on earth will I do when you return home, Row? Life won't be the same."

"That's why I'm telling you everything, Jay. I want you to come with me. You would have to leave your family and everything you know on Earth. Your body will change and you will become one of us. Powers will come over time, as you change.

"Your knowledge of Earth would be so helpful and you would make a brilliant teacher. Our planet is similar, with homes, schools, factories... except there is no crime or illness. People live forever. You won't be able to come back and see your family though, as you won't be able to materialise here the way we can, but you will be able to transmit thoughts to your family and friends as they sleep.

"It is something you'd have to think seriously about but you mustn't tell anyone."

After that, Row didn't mention it again.

One Saturday morning I visited Rowan with a smile on my face.

"Come on, Row, we are going for a bike ride. I have made my decision."

We rode out into the countryside, as always. We stopped at our favourite pub and sat on the grass in the sunshine with our bar meal.

I suddenly said, "I am coming with you. After a month of mulling it over I thought, what have I got to lose? It sounds a better life – no illness and no crime. I can teach. I have so much to offer."

"I was hoping you would say yes. You will love it there. My mother and father were both hoping you would come as well."

"When do we go?"

"Very soon," answered Row.

It was the following weekend when we made our way to a secluded spot. We parked our bikes and waited. It seemed like an eternity. Then suddenly a bright light engulfed us and we were lifted up.

"You are going to be fine," the paramedic said. "Your friend is OK as well. You skidded on the wet road. Your bikes aren't too good though. Glad to see you were both wearing the right gear. We will take you to hospital for a check-up but you both seem to be uninjured. You were very lucky."

"Oh no." Rowan shook his head. "This can't be true."

I looked at our bikes and saw how badly damaged they were, and yet we were both uninjured. This isn't right, I thought, how can it *all* have been a dream?

~~~

MIX 'N' MATCH CHARACTERS

Write a name on a slip of paper; fold it and pass it on.
Three more passes to add an age, occupation
and life-changing event.

The criteria the author had to work with
are given below each title.

...

Cyril's Shoes

Wendy Fletcher

Cyril Rogers;13; cobbler; won £1,000,000

Cyril was a good boy. Some said he was the best boy in the village. Since his mother died when he was three, he had lived with his father above the shop. He had learned from an early age to bounce up to the counter when the bell announced the arrival of a customer, a ready smile dancing on his lips, a light glowing in the innocent blue eyes and a polite greeting for all.

He had never gone through the unruly stage that a lot of families experienced with their children. The only unruly thing about Cyril was his hair – the mass of tumbling curls he had inherited from his poor mother. Perhaps his father was reluctant to have them cut because of this reminder, but Cyril didn't seem to mind. He just pushed them back when they spilled down his forehead and carried on, always humming a tune as he helped.

Cyril was thirteen now and considered himself to be a very lucky boy. He was an only child – sometimes wishing for siblings, but mostly glad that one day he would inherit the business and pass it on to his own children. As his father stitched leather and repaired shoes for locals from the surrounding villages, Cyril worked alongside him learning to stitch neatly and hand-polish the shoes for packing to go abroad.

This had been a new side-line for the business just a year ago but it was now doing really well. It had been one of Cyril's proudest moments when he announced to his father that he – a boy of just twelve at the time – had secured a contract to export shoes to England.

How it came about was a strange story. Cyril, through hard work and diligence, had won a scholarship to a good school, where he became a boarder. It meant spending less time here in the mountains, but he was fortunate to be chosen as that year's one child nominated to receive a free pass to go on the school trip. The destination was England and Cyril knew his father could never afford to send him on such an adventure. He had set out to learn everything about the culture of this strange country and make his father proud of him, but he never imagined how well it would go.

In fact, on the very first evening there was a moment when he feared it might have all gone terribly wrong. Somehow, in the crowded underground system, on the way to see a show, he had become separated from the rest of his party and was not on their train when it pulled out. Suddenly desperate and alone in this city he knew only as London, he jumped onto the next train and hoped to catch up.

That might have worked if he had been in his own country where two trains that headed in the same direction were likely to finish up at the same destination but this was London with its complex transport system. It even took Cyril underground, much to his wide-eyed horror.

At the first opportunity, he jumped off again and was darting along the platform in a growing panic when good luck caught up with him. A well-dressed man held out a hand to slow him and spoke kindly.

At once poor Cyril was reassured. He calmed down enough to enjoy a bacon roll and coffee in the café outside the station entrance. He knew he would have missed the show by now but it didn't seem important any more. His new companion recognised the name of Cyril's hotel and offered to have him driven home when he was ready. Meantime they sipped the hot coffee and chatted.

The man was interested in Cyril's family business and knew the area. He had friends there. Cyril told him as much detail as he could and the man seemed impressed.

By the time they parted company he had offered Cyril a deal that could be good for both of them. Cyril was to finish and pack the shoes to his normal high standards and send them to England where the man had a customer base. Cyril was so pleased with himself that he couldn't wait to tell his father.

The holiday had ended and school didn't seem so important now. His father's business had regular money coming in and a good contract. The future looked secure.

Cyril had returned to the shop full time and demand grew enough to keep them both employed. All day they worked side-by-side and late at night, when his father slept, Cyril worked on, his dreams stretching beyond the confines of this tiny shop. His heart leapt every time he recalled the words of the man in London, 'On the way to being a millionaire'.

One day they would own the whole street – maybe the whole village. Cyril imagined how many people they could help in this area where poverty often knocked on the door of local cottages. Sometimes he nearly burst with the excitement of it, because all could not yet be revealed.

Even his father wasn't completely in on the secret, but Cyril did understand how important it was that no-one stole the new recipe and shared it with competing shoe exporters.

At the moment the only people trusted with the secret were the man in England, who paid for the ingredients, the short man who delivered the product to the back door late at night and Cyril, who carefully sewed the tiny package of powder into the tongue of each shoe to ward off damp in transit, ensuring their arrival in England in a condition so perfect that they could not be beaten by any of their rivals.

~~~

Amos

Val Chapman

Amos; 92; chimney sweep; won a national writing competition.

Amos sat and looked around the room.

"By 'eck, this is a rum do," he mused, mostly to himself.

He never thought he'd find himself in a place like this.

With its heavy, plum-coloured curtains, sparkling chandeliers set into high ceilings, and luxuriously upholstered chairs – this was the kind of place Amos knew about, but had hardly ever been in.

Yet here he was, trussed up like a turkey in his best suit, and a fancy tie.

He hadn't worn a tie in years and wasn't keen on wearing one now.

There had been occasions when Amos had been somewhere fancy, like this – mainly with his beloved Sarah on their anniversary – but places like this weren't really for people like him.

"Aye, Sarah lass, you would have loved all this," he murmured quietly.

"What's that, Grandad? Were you talking to me? Do you want something?"

Amos looked up at his granddaughter, Elizabeth. Why did she have to shout at him? He wasn't deaf and he certainly wasn't stupid. Although, you'd think he was two pennies short of a shilling if you were to listen to her talking to him.

"No, you're all right lass, just thinking aloud, that's all. Is your mam or dad about?"

"They're just getting a couple more drinks I think. They'll be over soon. Dad'll make sure mum goes easy on the champagne, don't you worry."

Amos shook his head.

His daughter Annie was relishing all this, the kind of lifestyle she always dreamt of. It's a good job Gordon was here to keep an eye on her. He was a good man, thought Amos, hardworking and kind and, as son-in-laws went, he could have been worse.

He spotted Anne and Gordon making their way towards him.

The room was busy and Amos had hardly had a moment to himself. The world and his wife wanted to have a word with him, shake his hand or have a photo taken with him. They all said how brilliant he was, or how marvellous, and handed him another glass of champagne.

What's the matter with these folk, he wondered? The champagne was still untouched on the table in front of him, and if anybody bothered to ask him, he'd have a decent pint of Guinness, thank you very much!

His daughter was supposed to be bringing him one over, but she was enjoying herself too much, and all these bigwigs just thought everyone wanted the posh, fizzy stuff.

"Hi-ya Amos. How're you doing?" Gordon sat on the chair beside him.

"Annie's just taken our Elizabeth over to see Jamie Oliver – you know how much she likes him."

Oh aye, him. A 'celebrity chef,' if you please! What, in the name of all that is holy, is a celebrity chef?

He should try doing a proper job instead of mashing avocados, or whatever the latest fad was. There was nowt wrong with good old English food. Black pudding, or a nice bit of tripe – you couldn't beat it.

Nobody cooked a good Sunday roast nowadays. His wife's roast potatoes and Yorkshire puddings used to be the stuff of legend 'round the village.

After another few minutes of, "Ooh, Amos, you are amazing," and, "I hope I'm as good as you when I'm your age," the lights dimmed, and the chatter settled down to a quiet murmur.

A spotlight focussed on a small stage in the room, just in front of the table Amos was sharing with his daughter, son-in-law and granddaughter.

Amos looked across at Anne. How much she looked like her mother. The same chestnut hair and a little ski-jump of a nose. Her eyes were pure Amos though: big and blue – although his had faded over the years.

She was a bit loud and bossy now for Amos's liking, but he let his mind drift back through the years, remembering the young girl always dancing and twirling round their living room. She had a fancy for having her own dancing school, but Amos and Sarah could never find the money needed for that kind of thing.

Amos dragged himself back from memory lane in time to catch the end of a speech.

"And now, ladies and gentlemen, as you all know, our guest this afternoon is the wonderful, irrepressible, Amos Hardcastle, who joined his father as the local chimney sweep back in 1947, at the tender age of 13. A tough life, I'm sure you can imagine.

"Left to his own devices for much of the time, Amos kept a diary of his day-to-day life, and, trust me, there were many hilarious, and heartbreaking moments.

"Still working as a chimney sweep at the ripe old age of 75 – can you believe – he was persuaded by his granddaughter to turn some of these diary entries into a story.

"Ladies and gentlemen, it is this story that has taken the literary world by storm, and those of you who have read it will know exactly why.

"Amos Hardcastle is an inspiration to us all, and at 92, is proof that you're never too old to receive recognition for your success."

Amos was escorted to the stage by a pretty young lady he'd seen on the TV – Carole Vorderman, he thought her name was. Not that he needed assisting. He could still get about quite easily and – unlike one or two of his friends – still had one of his own hips.

The gentleman on stage – chief executive of the publishing house, if you please – smiled as he took Amos's hand.

"Such a pleasure to meet you again, Amos. As the oldest winner of our National Story-writing competition, do you have anything to share with the audience?"

Amos had been asked to prepare a little speech, which he delivered confidently, the audience laughing and commiserating at appropriate places. "Eating out of his hand," someone said later.

"And now I'll just say this. I may not have much of a future, but I've had a heck of a past."

The crowd stood and applauded. His family joined him on stage and Amos smiled as he looked at his daughter. Things had turned out pretty well for this Yorkshire chimney sweep.

"Now, can I have that Guinness?"

~~~

Peter Lewis

Stephen Oliver

Peter Lewis, 32, chef, involved in a serious car crash

Consider Peter Lewis.

He is a little over average height, slimly built, and 32 years old. He keeps his black hair short but stylish, parted on the right when it hasn't been pulled into a mess when he gets excited. His bright blue eyes have a direct gaze that some people find disconcerting.

Although he is fit, he doesn't go to the gym or exercise. He considers his work more than enough to keep his tendency to put on weight under control.

Consider Peter Lewis.

He left school at 16 to take up an apprenticeship at a well know restaurant where he trained as a chef. Part of the course consisted of one or two days a week at the local college, studying finance, planning, and everything else necessary to run your own place. Once he had qualified, he moved quickly up the ranks to become the senior sous chef.

Everything changed when a regular customer asked him to become her private chef at four times the admittedly good wages he was receiving.

He took her up on her offer and spent the next three years travelling around the world with her, cooking for her and her friends, wherever they might be. She was a demanding but fair boss, never asking the impossible but wanting only the best he could give. He feels that he grew tremendously during that time.

When she died, she left him a very generous bequest that, in addition to the wages that he had scrupulously saved, was more than enough for him to retire on. Instead, he took some of the money to set up his own catering company.

Consider Peter Lewis.

Now a successful caterer, he provides food for only the best and richest in the area. His initial investment has more than tripled since he started, and the waiting list for his services is now approaching a year.

He has several other chefs working for him, including his old boss from his first job. The team works well together, creating new items, and refining old ones, becoming the talk of an ever-increasing circle of customers.

Consider Peter Lewis.

You would have assumed that all this success might have gone to his head, but it hasn't. He is still a level-headed, modest individual, capable and talented, in charge of every aspect of his life.   Except one.

Consider Peter Lewis.

This is a man who lives in terror.

Every month, on the same day, ever since he can remember, he has had the same nightmare. He is involved in an accident, and there is red, *red*, **red** everywhere! In his dream, he believes it is his life's blood. It has distorted the pleasures of his life, which is why he never married.

Today is *that* day of the month, the one in which he wakes from his nightmare, but last night, he didn't dream it. That terrifies him even more. Could today be *the* day?

Consider Peter Lewis.

He has just been told that his driver, who was supposed to take him to a children's birthday party, has broken his leg and won't be at work today. Everyone else is out preparing for a gala dinner tonight.

Peter would have been on his way by now, had it not been for the phone call.

He is swearing and sweating as he gets behind the wheel of the van and starts the engine. He drives very carefully, hyper-vigilant and watching the traffic at every junction.

Despite this, he does not see the articulated lorry that jumps the lights and rams into his van, smashing into it at high speed.

Consider Peter Lewis.

He is lying on a stretcher, being attended to by paramedics and an ER doctor who happened to be passing by. They are examining him to determine just how severely injured he is. One of them is wiping his face with swabs, and each one is coming away red.

Once his face is clean, the doctor places a mask over his nose and mouth, and tells him to breathe in deeply.

"It's a mixture of oxygen and morphine," the doctor says. "It will help relieve the pain."

And there is a lot of pain. His back, chest and arms are all screaming at him, demanding his attention. More worrying, he cannot feel anything lower down. No awareness of toes, knees, or hips. In his hazy state, he wonders if he's a paraplegic.

The doctor keeps telling him everything will be fine, but sends anxious glances down the length of Peter's body from time to time. Peter can feel the pain ebbing away. The gas is working.

Consider Peter Lewis.

A constable is standing nearby, trying to take a statement from Peter, while another is talking to the lorry driver, who is in handcuffs.

As he looks around, Peter can see that the whole area is covered with bright red liquid. He didn't think a human being could have that much blood in him.

The two constables consult with one another, and one of them glances across at the ambulance. He is smiling.

"You know," he says to his colleague, "I've never seen so much strawberry jelly and cherry cola scattered across the road. It's going to take ages to clean the mess up."

Peter closes his eyes. He knows that it is not his blood after all.

He feels everything fade away as he takes another breath of the painkilling gas mixture.

Consider Peter Lewis, who has just died at the scene of the accident.

~~~

Mermaid Attendant

Phil Cumberland

Olivia Williams Holmes, 30yrs, Mermaid Attendant, broke a leg.

It was unusual for a mermaid attendant not to be a mermaid.

Olivia had always been fascinated by mermaids. Her childhood had been cluttered with the paraphernalia and memorabilia associated with mermaid literature and films, her bedroom walls papered with mermaid-patterned wallpaper, the windows fitted with mermaid-patterned curtains.

Mum, a placid, kind woman was sometimes driven to distraction by Olivia's obsession, hoping at some stage she would discover other interests: ponies, pop music, or even boys.

Olivia Williams Holmes progressed through school and university, gaining a BSc in marine and environmental science. Since leaving university in Bristol, her home town, she had a tried a number of different career paths, working in education, agriculture, and then marine conservation. Olivia still lived at home with her now widowed mum, her bedroom decor unchanged since a child despite mother's efforts to update it to something more neutral – or adult.

It was when climbing onto a survey vessel (a converted trawler), that Olivia broke her leg. The deck was wet. She slipped, fell awkwardly, and was stretchered off to hospital. Olivia loved the sea, and all that was within it. In her teens, she had wheedled and cajoled her dear old dad into setting up a marine aquarium, with fish, coral, shrimps and small hermit crabs.

Whilst recuperating from her broken leg, laid-up at home until she felt confident to resume work, her thoughts turned again to mermaids. Her return to work would be in a week or two; healing could continue as well in an office on light duties as it would at home dossing on the sofa.

Olivia had met her first mermaid on a university field trip to Malaysia, snorkelling along a coral reef, with a group of fellow students but separated from them. It was after observing a sea horse's erratic movements as it carried its egg that she broke surface to be confronted by a handsome bare-chested young man.

He was sitting on a rock that she didn't recall seeing earlier. Her eyes moved down his body but where his legs should have been there was, instead, a fish tail.

"Hello Olivia," he said in good English. "Glad you could make it."

Startled, Olivia somehow managed a hello. This should have been the realisation of her dreams but she was thoroughly non-plussed.

"I have been waiting for you to turn up," said the merman.

"Algernon – that is the seahorse you were watching – is a busy chap, but once he recognised you he let me know you were nearby."

Olivia's bewilderment increased by the second.

"How do you communicate with each other?" asked Olivia, "You have me at a complete disadvantage. What is your name?"

"I'm Sid. We marine creatures have an extra communication facility within us. You also have it, uniquely for a human, but at the moment are only able to transmit; you can't yet receive."

Olivia thought of the creatures in her marine aquarium. Two of the most interesting were a Gobi fish and Pistol shrimp. The two shared a symbiotic relationship, the blind Pistol shrimp lived in the sand at the bottom of the aquarium. It constructed tunnels in the sand, often using shells and shell fragments to strengthen them. His activities kept the sand clean.

The Gobi fish guarded the entrance to the tunnel under excavation, warning the shrimp of any perceived danger, at which point they would both hide in the tunnel with the shrimp guarding the entrance to protect the fish behind him.

Olivia had always wondered if they had any means of communicating other than touch.

During her time in Malaysia, she had further encounters with Sid, meeting members of his family and their wider community.

The Merfolk, as Olivia now thought of them, lived in the coral reef and in caves, both coastal and marine. By the time she returned to England, Olivia had begun to receive messages from the Merfolk, and communicate in a rudimentary way.

Bristol docks was the last place she expected to see a mermaid, but one morning Jennifer swam up to her dinghy and heaved herself up until her ample bosom rested on the boat's side.

Olivia had been expecting an encounter – they had been communicating telepathically for a week or two – but even so, Bristol was not Malaysia.

Jennifer opened the conversation with a "Good morning," then went on to ask if Olivia could help them, as an advocate for the Merfolk's interests in the world.

"The job will be advertised," Jennifer continued, "but applicants will need to know where to look and have the means to get in touch. You have the means to get in touch, thanks, largely, to Sid.

"The advertisement will appear in the Telegraph next Wednesday, in the small ads within the vacancies section. It will be written in such a way that only those with the right skills will be able to read it."

With that Jennifer bade farewell, lowered herself gently back into the water and swam off.

Olivia continued to the trawler, climbed the ladder fixed to it, clambered over onto the deck, slipped and, in falling, broke her leg.

On Wednesday, Mum had fetched her the Telegraph, surprised that Olivia hadn't asked for the Guardian.

There, within the small ads of the employment section, was the advertisement: MER, ATT, REQ, CONT, S, 4, DET, USUAL CHANNEL.

Olivia contacted Sid, and the job was hers.

Once the leg had healed, Olivia travelled back to Malaysia and started working for the Merfolk. Her mum soon joined her, and they lived contentedly in a quiet coastal village.

That was when Olivia began to write – not only her children's stories, featuring Crystal the Mermaid, but more serious books.

Her ground-breaking work on the infrastructure of coral reefs and the marine communities within them, were informed by first-hand observation, making them a huge commercial success.

~~~

The Midwife

Jan Cunningham

Cyril (Cy) Thompson; 38; deliveries; Wife left, lost job.

"Now, pant! Christine! Pant! Pant! Pant! Well done. With your next contraction, push like you've never pushed before. Like, it's the biggest constipated poo ever."

"Shut up Cy, I can't giggle and push at the same time. Ooooooooh here we go."

"Just one more and you'll be able to say Hello to Missy. Here she comes. Oh! She is so beautiful."

And with that, Cy cleared the baby's airways and popped her on Christine's tummy. Then followed the cries of happiness and joy from the new parents.

Out at the Nurses Station, Anna commented to another midwife.

"I don't know how Cy does it. When he joined us, I thought there would be ructions. I mean – a male midwife – whatever is the world coming to?

"We all thought midwifery was the last bastion of female domination."

"I know," said Greta. "But he's so respectful and gentle, especially with new mums-to-be, that not one has refused to have him deliver her.

"I think a lot of his charm is because he is older – and no George Clooney – therefore presenting no obvious threat to the dads-to-be. And he has a lovely dry sense of humour."

"Only problem is Naomi; she can't stand him. Don't know why. P'raps she thinks, because he's a man, he'll get preferential treatment when it comes to promotion. There's that Senior Midwife post coming up soon and she's desperate to get it."

The remainder of the late shift passed peacefully.

"Coming for a quick one, Cy?" asked Anna. "I sure am ready for a large glass of cold Chardonnay on a Friday night."

"Yeah, why not," answered Cy. "Nothing to rush home for."

"Your wife still at her Mum's?" enquired Greta, as she linked arms with Anna and Cy. They danced down the main concourse and out of the door of the hospital.

"Yes. She'll be staying for a while."

He couldn't tell them his wife had left him months ago. Too much information – especially as the hospital grapevine would have a field day... Why had she left? Whose fault was it? Can he afford to keep their lovely house?

He couldn't cope with their sympathy – or pity, depending on who was giving it.

He didn't really understand why Joanne had left him. He knew she was fed up with all the hours he worked, but she had known how he felt about his job before they married. She accused him of always putting his career before her but – as it was *her* who wanted the foreign holidays and nice house – how did she think they could afford them, unless he worked his socks off?

Not that he minded. He loved his work with a passion. To be there at the beginning of a life, to see the little one safely into this world and know he had done his utmost to make the birth as good as he could for baby, mother and father too, made him feel proud and humble at the same time. There was no better feeling in this world.

He arrived home to another pile of red utility bills and a council tax demand, plus another letter from the mortgage company telling him to pay up or they will have no option but to repossess the house.

Shoving all the envelopes into a drawer, he poured himself a large whisky.

Life goes on. Cy was as dedicated and professional as always, but Anna and Greta began to worry. At times he seemed distant – not his usual cheery self.

One Monday, following a particularly gruelling weekend on shift, Cy arrived at the unit and was immediately called to the manager's office.

"There has been a complaint made against you, for harassment and bullying," said Jane Cotton, the unit manager, unable to look him in the eyes.

Cy's face drained and he whispered, "Who?"

"I'm not at liberty to say.

"So could you now just get your things and go home. You may not talk to any of the staff. I will let you know the outcome of the investigation when it's taken place."

With that Jane sat down and turned back to her computer.

Cy was devastated. Only that morning the mortgage company had issued him with a repossession order, and now this.

He walked out of Jane's office, looking straight ahead. Ignoring the questions and stunned looks from his workmates when he said he was suspended, he collected his things and walked home in a daze.

The days dragged on and on. Cy couldn't eat or sleep. He stopped washing or shaving. The house was a mess... but it was being repossessed, so who cared?

One morning, he packed a rucksack with a few possessions, walked out of the door, pushed the keys through the letterbox and walked into town. When night came he found himself back outside the hospital, having no idea how he got there. He settled down in a doorway at the back that was hardly ever used. He took a bottle of water from his rucksack and washed down the pills he had saved, knowing this day would come.

Next morning, as Greta wandered past the back of the hospital to reach the main door, she saw something lying there and went to investigate. She looked down, screamed, and went running into the hospital.

"Someone – anyone – please come and help," she yelled. "Cy's lying outside, and I don't like the look of him!"

Naomi was arriving and, hearing Greta's anguished cries, went hurtling through the door with her. When they reached Cy's body, Naomi bent down, then shook her head. Cy was dead.

"Why? Oh God why!" cried Greta. "His suspension was being lifted today – no case to answer. Hope the miserable bitch that reported him rots in hell!"

Naomi swallowed hard, then turned and walked away.

~~~

Don't Look Down

Cathy Cade

Xander Curtis; 35; window cleaner; fell off fishing boat, almost died.

Xander Curtis looked down; he couldn't help himself. The ground drew his gaze like a magnet. He wobbled. In thirty-five years, he couldn't remember wobbling on a ladder before.

He was aware of every metre of nothingness between him and the ground – whether he looked or not. He wasn't afraid of hitting it; he'd never been afraid of that. He was afraid it would absorb him, swallow him. Suffocate him.

His foot groped for the rung beneath him. Carefully, he transferred his weight onto it.

Carol was in the kitchen when he got home; she was working the evening shift today.

'You're early,' she said. 'Is it raining again?'

'No. I'm feeling tired. Knackered. Maybe I overdid it yesterday.'

His wife was instantly concerned.

'We shouldn't have gone out the day before you started back. We should have made it next weekend.'

They had gone out to celebrate his full recovery and forthcoming return to work. Now she looked anxious again.

'Maybe you should be building up to it gradual-like.'

But he knew he was as fit, physically, as he had ever been. Fitter – he'd spent long enough in the gym. He dropped onto a kitchen chair.

'I'm shattered. I'll try again tomorrow. After a good night's sleep.'

His tic flickered. It wasn't visible to an observer – he could only see it if he looked closely in the mirror at the right time. Sometimes resting a finger on it would calm it.

He closed his eyes behind cool fingers, shutting out Carol's frown, and the bills waiting in the letter-rack.

Carol had spent hours delivering leaflets to customers to explain his absence. Most had remained loyal and the bank had extended their overdraft. While Carol worked extra shifts at the supermarket, his mum had collected the boys from school and taken them at weekends.

At least, since he'd been home from hospital, he could do that himself. He hadn't taken them swimming yet... but they'd played football in the garden and cycled to the park. There was no real reason for him to postpone his return to work as long as he had. Something held him back.

After tea, the boys settled to their homework in the kitchen while Carol loaded the dishwasher. In the living room, he turned on the television to a news report of a father who'd drowned in Spain trying to rescue his daughter. The memory rose again to swamp him.

They'd been visiting Carol's family in Fife. He had taken so long strapping the boys into their lifejackets, he hadn't got around to fastening his own. His brother-in-law's fishing boat was old, with a high cabin – it had seemed high when he pitched off the top of it. Thrown clear of the boat, he seemed to be a long time in the air, watching the water approach. The freezing shock of it stunned him, as if he had hit hard ground, but it didn't stop him falling further... down and down. Although his legs thrashed, the light still receded above him. Eventually, his descent had slowed and he paused... suspended for too long before starting to rise – too slowly, and too late. His lungs craved air and he gave up fighting.

They told him his brother-in-law got him to the boat as the harbour lifeboat arrived and emergency services took over. In a coma for days, it was weeks before he transferred to a hospital near home. Recovery was slow, but he *had* recovered. He had been lucky.

'You can do this if you don't look down,' he told himself. The trouble was, he didn't believe himself. Yesterday had confirmed fears he hadn't dared to acknowledge.

He'd completed the ground floor first – working from bottom to top instead of front to back, the way he'd always worked. Putting it off.

But now it was time for the ladder.

He looked up. The higher he climbed, the further he would sink when he fell. The ground would absorb him, swallow him, suffocate him, as the sea had. With eyes on the brickwork behind the rungs, he started to climb.

Both hands gripped cold metal. He used to do this one-handed. Now, the bucket swung from his arm, banging against the ladder. He paused.

He looked down – he couldn't help himself.

Gravity tugged at every movement, mocking him. What was he going to do now – peddle his service to bungalow-dwellers? His eyelid squirmed.

What use was a window cleaner afraid of heights?

ALMOST FAMILIAR

Take a familiar title and give it a twist

.

...

Star Truck: a Star Trek Fanfiction Spoof

Stephen Oliver

"The engines canna take it, Cap'n," Scotchy, the engineer shouted from the back of the ship – the intercom was on the fritz again. "Yer overloading them."

"I haven't even started them," Lieutenant Silly complained from the helm. He pointed. "See, the key's not in the ignition at all."

Captain Jimmy Z Crickit sighed. He hated it when his crew started bickering before they even left a planet. But what could you expect when you were the commander of the interstellar haulage ship *Underpriced*, infamous for being late, if it actually arrived at all?

Right now, they were stuck on some gods-forsaken backwater planet, waiting for the customs officers to get off their multiple butts and let them load their cargo. He had already greased their palms with Syrian Vodkatini and ten packets of Wrigley's Spearmint (which was a hallucinogenic aphrodisiac for them), but it apparently wasn't enough. He had been metagoogling the Ultranet for some clues on what else it would take when this little argument broke out.

"Look, guys, it's not our fault the wrap drive didn't work near that black hole," he said. "Stupid Galactic Positioning System didn't tell us to divert around it. They're always forgetting to send out updates."

He stopped as a thought crossed his mind. Turning to his science officer, he continued. "You *did* remember to order the update, didn't you?"

First Officer Spork nodded.

"Yes, Sir. It took a while for it to arrive because they sent it to Alderaan, and not Aldebaran. But I was able to install it before we left."

He punched a couple of keys on his control panel and the copyright information appeared on the main screen.

"As you can see, Captain, it is less than half a stardate old."

"Chust a minute, Sirr," Ensign Kickoff looked up from the map he was trying to refold unsuccessfully. "Vhat's that symbol in the bottom rright corrnerr?"

Crickit squinted as he looked at the cracked corner.

"Damnation, they sent us the beta version again. No wonder it didn't show that the black hole had wandered into Frienderation space. Lieutenant O'Hula, I want you to report it to the authorities at once."

"I can try," she muttered.

"What was that?"

"I said, 'I'm on it,' Sir."

She began twiddling the dials, switching from FM to AM when she couldn't find anything.

"I can't get through, Sir. There's some sort of interference coming from that building over there."

She pointed out of the window. Crickit put his head in his hands.

"Lieutenant, that 'building over there' is the customs shed. They probably want to talk to us and tell us there's another delay. Put them on the main screen."

"Ah, Captain Crickit," said the tall pile of pink and green tinsel on the screen. "You may load with immediate effect. This is good stuff... gurgle... bloep... wordleflop... groop."

The last thing they saw was a string of reflective material holding a gum wrapper up to the screen.

Crickit turned to the crew.

"Get to it, guys, before it sobers up and changes its mind."

Six hours later, the engines proved that they could take it as the *Underpriced* prised itself loose from the soil and lumbered spacewards.

As they cleared the atmosphere, Crickit turned to Spork.

"Have you managed to get the GPS working?"

"Yes, Sir. They sent an emergency update via Direct Hyper-Light courier, with their deep-felt apologies."

"I bet."

"Apparently, they were already working on it after the Frienderation Frigate *Balls O' Fire* disappeared down the black hole."

"So, it's up to date."

"I hope so."

"You? Hope? That's an emotion, you know, Spork. I thought you didn't have any."

"They sneak up on me from time to time, Sir. I'll go and have a lie down until it's over."

"Later, Spork. I want you on deck for now. It's time to go into wrap drive."

"Very well, Sir."

"Navigator, Helmsman, I want you to get us faster than light faster than you did last time."

"Yes, Sir," Silly and Kickoff answered.

Kickoff opened up his newly folded map again and turned it around and around, looking for their destination.

Meanwhile, Silly spun the ship around to point in what he hoped was the right direction, triggering nausea in every being aboard.

"All set, Sirr," Kickoff said. He had the finger of one hand on the map while he punched in a 60-digit number with the other.

"Make it so," Crickit said. Everyone looked at him.

"Sorry," he said. "I have no idea where that came from. Let's kick this old bucket of bolts in the backside and see if we can get our cargo to its destination without it fermenting."

He shuddered, remembering the last time they had transported Deneb-Garr grapes that were a *little* overripe. They had been hungover for the whole week-long journey. He brightened. On the other hand, the three-day drunk afterwards, while they were coming down again, had been fantastic.

He watched the lights on the screen as the wrap-nacelles extended out from the sides of the ship. Brown paper extruded from them as they spun around the ship, followed by sticky tape and string. Lastly, the label with their address was applied. The ship then slipped itself into the waiting slot in PostSpace and vanished from the skies.

As they were being bumped around by the other ships in this microcosmic sack, Crickit grimaced to himself.

There must be a better way of doing things, he thought. Maybe something to do with bending space around the ship?

They had been underway for three days when they heard the distress call.

"Captain, a ship is calling for help," O'Hula said. "Something about an infestation. They want medical assistance, and we're the only one with a doctor on board."

"If you can call him that," Crickit muttered to himself.

"Okay, drop us out of wrap and see what we can do. When will we be in range?"

"In about two seconds, Sirr," Kickoff said and pressed the big red 'Stop' button.

With a loud thump, the *Underpriced* was dropped from the sack and came to a shuddering halt. Torn brown paper, string and sticky tape floated away from the ship. Everyone fought the desire to throw up.

Half a mile away, a lumpy pile of dirt floated in space.

"Oh dear," Silly said. "That looks like it's a Crudistani ship. Better put your wellies on, Captain."

"I will." Crickit stood up. "Silly, you have the con. Spork, you're with me." He walked out of the control room.

Kickoff glared across at Silly.

"Vhy do you always ket the con?" he hissed.

"Because I'm senior to you, so there!" Silly gloated.

Crickit's first stop was his quarters, where he put his fishing waders on before pocketing a nose clip. This would not be the first time he had been on a Crudi ship. The inhabitants of that planet were hive-creatures, so the crew would be all female, meaning that he would be wading through piles of soft wipes and scented cloths.

He left his cabin and walked down the corridor to the san.

He hoped to gods that Moans hadn't been sampling his own 'medicines' again. He was in luck. The medic was sober.

"We have an emergency on another ship," Crickit told him.

"Does that mean we're going to stream over?" Moans looked excited at the prospect as he picked up his pink bag. He preferred the colour to black.

"Yes, we are," Crickit replied, sounding grumpy. There was a good reason he hated the Displacer.

As they went down the corridor, Crickit grabbed a passing crewman.

"I need you to help me in an emergency, O'Reilly."

"Okay, Sir," The man fell into step with him.

"What on earth happened to your shirt, O'Reilly? It's bright red."

"I'm sorry, Sir. I left some Centauran cherries in the pocket, and the colour ran. Not to mention the crud they left behind got caught in my hair. I had to shave it all off."

"Oh, I see. Well, try not to be so forgetful next time."

"No, Sir."

They walked into the Displacer room and stepped into the booths. They nodded to the technician at the controls to say they were ready.

Crickit cringed as the Blender blades stuck out from all sides. It didn't hurt as their atoms were taken apart, but the thought of being chopped up like this always depressed him.

The resulting subatomic paste was squeezed out of the booths and electronically blasted across to the other ship.

As always, it seemed to Cricket that nothing had happened to him, but the world had jumped around him. He looked down to check that all his parts were still there.

Damn, he thought, I'd better get Scotchy to check the system. It's given me plaid trousers again.

At least that was better than the last time. He had ended up wearing a pastel pink toga, which was see-through in all the wrong places.

The captain of the Crudistani ship was waiting for them as they reassembled. She was small and dainty, resembling a four-foot tall ladybird.

"Thank you for coming, Captain," she chirped. "We have an outbreak of Flurges. The culprit is one of the passengers, on her way to her wedding."

Crickit looked across at the science officer.

"Flurges are the inhabitants of Betegeuse 7," Spork explained. "They're slug-like creatures that are normally slow and—" He hesitated for a moment.

"Sluggish?" O'Reilly suggested with a grin.

Moans glared at him. Puns were his thing, and he hated competition.

"The problem is, Captain," the Crudi exclaimed, "it's her mating season. She's never mated before, so she is out of control. She has already eaten half of my crew."

"How do Flurges mate?" Crickit asked, afraid to ask.

"They eat their mates whole, then extract the necessary genetic material from the body as they absorb it. She will continue until she finds male genes. You are the only males on the ship."

The three men paled visibly. Spork was already pale because he was, after all, vulcanised.

"Are you armed?" she asked.

"Of course." Crickit pulled his fazer out. "It's designed to confuse an enemy. We're not allowed to carry anything more dangerous."

"Ah, I see," the Crudi said. "Frienderation rules, of course."

"No," Crickit replied. "We're just too trigger-happy and like shooting things." They walked down the corridor together, towards sounds of screaming.

Suddenly, their noses were assaulted by the stench of rotting cabbage, which overwhelmed the background miasma of patchouli and lavender.

"I believe those are the pheromones of the Flurge species," Spork declared.

At that moment, the creature slurped around the corner, holding a Crudi in each of her two main pseudopods.

As soon as she saw them, she let out a complex, multi-toned screech. "Males," she screamed. "There are males on board. Come to Mummy-to-be!"

They all fired their fazers, but to no avail. The Flurge was too big and too crazed to be disconcerted by anything. She rushed towards them as they backed away.

O'Reilly wasn't looking where he was going, and tripped over a neatly piled stack of soft wipes. He sprawled on his back as the others fled.

The Flurge was on him in a moment. Its pseudopods shot out and grabbed him, dragged him upright, and pulled him up to the front of her bulk.

"Male, yummy," the creature said.

Its front opened up as a huge orifice, which engulfed the unfortunate crewman. He disappeared with a cut-off scream.

Immediately, the Flurge sagged against the wall and began humming to itself in a *basso profundo* voice, eyes half-closed with a sated look.

The others watched from a distance.

"Is she safe now?" Crikit asked the Crudi captain.

"Yes, but I think her groom might be a little upset that he will not be the one to be eaten on his marriage night."

Moans was eyeing the creature. "You said this one had never mated before. Is that right?"

"Yet, it is," the Crudi chirped.

"And I believe this is the first time Humanity and Flurge have met."

"I think you may be correct, doctor," Spork said.

"In that case, Captain, you could say that he has baldly gone where no man has gone before."

~~~

I Walk the Lane

Wendy Fletcher

I walk the lane, more sedately now,
where once I skipped, a child without a care.
I breathe again the scents of summer,
the blossom lightly drifting in the air,

Today I am alone with the birds
as they arc and soar above my head,
Casting shadows on the dusty path
where my silent, lonely footsteps tread.

The hedges draped in May will always
be those bridal gowns of ivory lace
that he showed to me so long ago
beside this ancient lane, our special place.

On the bank grows the cow parsley that
he said were their silken, slippered feet.
With the pert bells of nettles, each sown
to decorate the toe with stitches neat.

Those Ox-eye Daisy maids of honour
willowy on slender stems of green,

Tall above the Poppy flower girls
in scarlet frocks, reaching to be seen.

A carpet of bluebells, nodding their heads
in harmony to point the way,
are once again the drift of confetti
at that wedding in a long-ago May.

And as I walk the lane on my own
I feel his touch and hear his voice so mild.
I live once more the stories that he told
to me, his precious only child.

Father, I miss you, but this is where
I come to feel you close, to heal the pain,
Knowing you will always be here with me
to share the joys as I walk the lane.

~~~

Budget Holiday

Philip Cumberland

We spent an eventful first night of our budget holiday playing Bash the Bed Bug. The beds were so old the maker's name on the worm-eaten headboard was written in Latin. The one small mercy was there were no springs sticking out of the mattress; they had all been removed and melted down to make cannons for the Napoleonic wars.

After a fitful night's sleep, we staggered down the rickety stairs of our decrepit hotel to breakfast. The kitchen was like the three witches scene from Macbeth but being a budget hotel there was only one in the cast. She was stirring porridge in a black iron pot over an open fire. No doubt, rumours about the invention of gas cookers had reached the hotel management but they placed such stories within the realms of fantasy.

Eventually breakfast was served. Only great will-power and ravenous hunger enabled us to devour the offering put before us. Compared to this establishment, Greasy Joe's transport café was a three star Michelin restaurant.

Although there was no eye of toad or leg of newt in the porridge, one sensed their presence. After a chipped mug of black tea we completed our breakfast.

Following a quick sluice down from the galvy cold water bucket – the en-suite to our room – we were ready for the sight-seeing tour.

I don't know whose idea it was to include the tour of the abattoir in the day's itinerary but it was not an obvious choice. We were very nervous about the other excursions promised in the brochure; all were listed as mystery tours. I suppose the biggest mystery was how the company had avoided prosecution. The only saving grace was that we had booked the short three-night break not the full week's offering.

We returned to our quarters worn out from the sight seeing tour and from bump-starting the 1927 Leyland charabanc – our transport for the day. We wearily trudged upstairs to our bedroom to scrape off the blood and entrails, which were a memento of the slaughter house tour. Although bump-starting the bus had been tiring – particularly the half-mile push up the one-in-five to give us a start on the down-side of the hill – it did give us a chance to get some fresh air, allowing the wind to blow away the putrid smell that clung to us like a dog to a favourite bone. The driver had kept the handbrake on to stop the bus rolling back down the hill on top of us but it made the bus a devil of a job to push.

The wizened crone who acted as hotel cook had excelled herself; the steak and kidney pudding was excellent. The absence of one stocking gave us a clue to how the pudding was wrapped for cooking.

After several brown ales we retired for the night, too tired to put up a fight with the wildlife sharing our bed. There is less biodiversity in Barnsley zoo than in that bed.

We awoke early, scratching away the small creatures of the night that stuck to our skin with the steadfastness of a bank manager clutching a newly-signed mortgage agreement. After scraping our skins, use of the galvy bucket and copious amounts of coal tar soap, we made our way down for breakfast. It was probably the smell of burning bacon that had woken us. It is very unusual to see black bacon. Crispy bacon is not uncommon, but to achieve a near cremation without the result turning completely to ash is a remarkable achievement.

We boarded the Leyland ready for another day of excitement, unsure whether to expect a tour of a sewerage works, a tanning factory or an industrial laundry. Ecclestone's Brewery was, therefore, a surprising destination. Ecclestone's is an old-fashioned brewery. There is much steam, whirring shafts, open machinery and flapping drive belts. Power is provided to the works by a very ancient steam engine, its low chimney belching copious amounts of black smoke to descend on all and sundry in the damp air as wet soot.

The tour was going relatively well until a posse of rats pursued by three ginger tom cats hurtled by. They raced around the floor, then up in the machinery before two rats fell into a huge vat squealing horribly. The elderly tour guide didn't bat an eyelid.

One of the men in our group asked about the incident.

"That often happens," explained our guide calmly. "The rats can't keep a grip on the damp surfaces so they fall in the vat."

Another member of the group asked how the brewery dealt with the situation.

"When we empty the vat we strain the rats out and dispose of them."

"What about the rats?" he asked.

"Oh, they are quite dead."

"What about the beer?"

"It's alright, they don't drink a lot of it; you see, they only have small stomachs and if they can't get out they drown. If they do get out they are usually so intoxicated the cats catch them easily."

The party shuffled their feet, looking uneasy. One or two had turned quite green and seemed in danger of vomiting.

Our man continued, unperturbed, "But surely that isn't very healthy."

"Not for the rats, no, but the cats are more sensible and keep away from the open vat."

"But what about the quality of the beer?" our man persisted.

"I'll get you a glass and you can try it yourself and let me know what you think."

"What, when it has had rats in it?"

"It's alright; they have been strained out, like I said before."

At the tour's end, everyone declined the offer of a free pint and seemed relieved to be returning to the hotel. There was a great deal of nervousness, however, when we learned that Toad in the Hole was the dish for dinner. The relief was palpable when Toad in the Hole turned out to be sausages in Yorkshire pudding.

We decided to leave straight after dinner, foregoing the pleasure of another night in the wildlife park that had been our bed and the culinary delights of next day's breakfast.

If it had been possible to award minus stars in the review of our holiday, the minus fifty mark would easily have been surpassed. All I can say is, even if you are offered good money, do not take one of Earnest Mugroach's "Heritage Tours of the North".

~~~

The Mitherers

Jan Cunningham

Well, to be honest I never thought of it as murder. To me, I was just doing them a favour, giving a little help to speed things up. I mean, those poor relatives hanging around day after day, often week in week out, in limbo-land, whilst their loved ones took their own sweet time to go.

And could they mither? The relatives, that is. The patients hardly said a word seeing as how they were barely conscious. Their relations could mither for England, and who could blame them? I mean, what else had they to do? It's so boring, waiting – however much you love 'em.

So, being the kind and generous-hearted person I pride myself on being, and being in a position to help them, I did.

It wasn't till Mrs R gave me a cheque for £500 for services rendered, "Over and above... and Mr R would have wanted it," that it got me thinking. I could do with a pension plan 'cos with my wages there was no 'ope.

Anyway, I started to pay more attention to what the mitherers were on about. You know the sort of things – how you couldn't afford to buy a house of your own anymore; the cost of living; kids wanting the latest gizmos, etcetera. So I started joining in, instead of just listening, with an occasional, "Really," and "Fancy that," and let them know how hard it was for me, what with my flat rent going up again, the high cost of petrol and don't get me started on the price of 'lecy and gas.

But I never moaned or complained about all the *extra* time I gave them, doing all the little *extras* they wanted, 'cos I love my job and will always do my best for my patients.

I never asked for money directly. I couldn't do that, it would've been unprofessional, but a small (and very occasionally, large) thank-you was most acceptable. And you know how people love to gossip... and these support groups the mitherers were encouraged to attend were a godsend to me 'cos it soon got around that I was the best.

And so it started. Not every time – 'cos not everyone could, depending on their circumstances, and others were just plain greedy or tight – but often enough for me to start my pension plan.

You see it's quite easy for me, in my position, to administer a little more morphine than the stated dose each time, and speed things up. I thought I was doing everyone a favour, patient included (others may think differently). But they were all grateful when the end came, especially as it was a bit quicker than expected.

See, satisfaction all round. Patient no longer

suffering and relatives getting their hands on the inheritance quicker, with often a little thank-you to me. Win-win I'd say.

I'm not daft; I didn't rush it. I didn't overdose blatantly. As I did the ordering and collection of repeat prescriptions, I could gradually bring re-order dates a little bit earlier than they should have been. Then the next one a little bit earlier again, so no-one noticed at the surgery that the morphine stocks were getting low quicker than usual. Anyway, the Doctors are so overworked nowadays, poor loves, coupled with the fact they hardly – if ever – visited my patients, 'cos there was nothing they could do for them – being terminal and that. They never queried anything. To be honest, I think they were glad to have someone like me to save them the bother.

Over the years, I built up my pension fund to quite a tidy little nest egg. I took advice and invested some of it – which, as it happens, is doing rather well. I knew it couldn't last forever. One day some jobsworth would come along and figure it out. Well, I wasn't going to stay around for that, was I? So I took early retirement.

And here I am. On my second world cruise and loving every minute of it. Course you wouldn't recognise me now. I have a new name and passport, beautiful straight white teeth (just like Americans), got my eyes lasered so no glasses, had my hair cut and highlighted professionally, and spent quite a few bob on health farms to help me lose weight, detox and all that malarkey.

Amazing what money can do.

The other night I met a couple in the bar. We chatted away – or rather, Mr Rose-Call-me-Fred did most of the talking. Or mithering, as I'd call it. They were on their first cruise and, according to Fred, their last since Avril was terminally ill. Well, well, well, I thought. Fancy that. My pension could do with a top-up. And Fred was always mithering on about how much care Avril demanded, how he wasn't a nurse and what about his holiday?

So you can imagine the rest can't you? And as her end came quicker than he'd anticipated – leaving him free to enjoy the rest of his holiday – his thank-you was one of the biggest I'd received.

Well, that started me thinking again. There must be others like the Roses where I could make my services invaluable – and them rich enough to thank me appropriately. It was just a matter of research. I could pick and choose who, where and when, and have plenty of holidays in between.

After this cruise, I'm going to keep a look-out for the mitherers.

~~~

Gone With the Wine

Val Chapman

"How much did we used to spend on wine?"

"Oh, I guess about half an hour."

"Ha-ha, Silly. What do you think – should we go for red or white?"

"It doesn't matter, they're both decent. I don't think Ashley would sell anything else."

"Good point. I'll get both."

Tara grinned. Grasping one bottle in each hand, she made her way to the counter. Her husband, Rick, followed with a resigned sigh, picking up a family-sized pack of cheese and onion crisps on the way.

"Ah, Mr and Mrs Butler, how are you both this evening?"

Ashley Wilkes had known the couple for a few years now. They were regular visitors at his wine merchant shop although, to be fair, he saw much more of Tara's mother, Vivian, than he did Tara and Rick.

Aware that he should keep that little snippet to himself, he made sure to keep things on a professional level whilst in the shop, especially in front of Tara and the other couple of customers who were deliberating over a Shiraz or Malbec.

"Ah, very good choices, Mrs Butler."

"Why thank you, Ashley, my mother said she might call round later after her yoga class, and she always claims to have something to either celebrate, or commiserate. So these are bound to come in handy."

Rick was about to pay.

"Oh God, I forgot about Vivian coming round. I might have to take another couple of bottles. You've met her; you know what she's like."

"Maybe you shouldn't encourage her, Mr Butler, although I must admit she has been good for business over the last couple of years, and one really mustn't judge."

"I know, I know, we shouldn't, but you know that saying – 'Walk a mile in their shoes'? Well, if you walked a mile in her shoes, you'd end up in a wine bar!" He packed the bottles into a box.

"Ashley, I honestly don't know what to do with the woman, she's turning into a right lush, but Tara can't seem to see it. We're going to have to be tougher with her. She just doesn't respond to the 'nicey-nicey' approach."

After a few pleasantries, Rick joined Tara in their car and drove the short distance to the house.

Tara still experienced a thrill when she walked up to their front door.

The cottage had been a bit sad and neglected when they bought it five years ago, but now it was perfect, right down to the shiny front door in her favourite shade of blue. Even better than she had imagined when they first embarked on making it their ideal home. It meant they both had to work longer hours to pay for work to be done, but it had been bearable, and living through the mess had definitely been worth it.

The couple were thrilled with it, and had started talking about the "patter of tiny feet," even though Rick was thinking "dog" while Tara was thinking "cat". They felt life was pretty good for Tara and Rick Butler right now.

The only fly in the ointment was Tara's emotionally draining mother, but they were working on it – for all the good it appeared to be doing.

After they had eaten and cleared away the evidence of Tara's tuna pasta bake, they took the rest of the wine bottle into the living room, settled into their new sofa and switched on the TV.

"Oh, look, it's that new drama with whatshername in it. We were looking forward to watching it, remember? I'd forgotten it was tonight."

Ten minutes in, and there was a knock on the door.

Tara and Rick looked at each other, silently asking, "Who might that be?" and "Are you going to answer it, or am I?"

A fraction of a second later and their eyes widened as realisation dawned,

"Oh hell – mother."

"Oh hell – Vivian."

"I'll get it," said Rick. "You never know your luck, it might be someone else. Keep your fingers crossed it's a serial killer or something, instead."

"Darling, how are you both?"

Vivian swept past Rick and headed for the lounge. She folded herself neatly into an armchair and called out to Rick.

"Red, please, Rick – the bigger the better. After the day I've had, I need it."

Vivian let out a sigh and closed her eyes.

Tara turned off the TV and folded her arms, looking across at her mother.

"What's the matter now?"

"Oh, Tara darling, where to start?"

Rick returned to the lounge, glass in hand.

"I noticed your car outside Vivian so I poured you a small one. Besides, it's all that's left in the bottle."

Tara's mother turned towards Rick,

"Oh darling boy, surely you know size really does matter? No one wants a *small* glass of wine.

"Anyway, I called in to see Ashley on the way here and picked up a couple of bottles. He is such a lovely man. And I can always stay in the spare room if I over-indulge."

With a resigned sigh, Tara sat back and listened to her mother's tale of woe, which – as far as she could work out – consisted of the tree surgeon arriving late and charging too much, and the yoga instructor leaving after next week's class.

"But you don't understand, darling. I couldn't possibly go to a class run by Nadim. His ideas are simply outrageous. He just doesn't do things the way they should be done – the way Melanie does them. Maybe I should hire my own personal tutor. Tara, sweetheart, what do you think?"

"It hardly matters, does it?" Tara replied. "When have you ever listened to my opinion?"

Tara despaired of her mother. She wafted around in a world of her own, expecting people to attend to her every whim. Since the work on their cottage was finished, Vivian seemed to assume it was another place of residence for her. It was as much as Tara and Rick could do to keep her from claiming the master bedroom for her own when she stayed over.

"But it overlooks the best part of the garden," she had said. "It would be so restful for my nerves."

Over the past weeks – indeed, months – she had been spending more time with Tara and Rick – after she had popped in to Ashley's shop they suspected – and they were beginning to realise how needy and manipulative Vivian was. At times, she was hard to say no to, but they resolved to put on a united front and stand up to her.

It helped that they had an ally in Ashley. He seemed to understand, and could offer advice, or – more usually – something to drown their sorrows if they seemed to be losing control. They knew, of course, the answer didn't lie at the bottom of a bottle, but, as her mother was fond of pointing out, "You can at least try!"

Vivian had ignored her daughter's last comment. "Do you know what would go well with this wine?"

"I'm sure you'll tell us."

"Some more of this wine!" Vivian leant back in the chair, and roared with laughter.

Rick and Tara looked at each other. It wasn't that funny, but at least it took Vivian's mind off her "troubles".

"I said that to Ashley earlier, and he thought it was a genius remark.

"Actually, I have been spending some time with darling Ashley lately, and I have made a decision."

Her daughter and son-in-law looked first at each other, then back at Vivian. She wasn't known for making the wisest of decisions; heaven only knows what she wanted to do now.

"I'm going to invest in Ashley Wilkes and his wine emporium."

Oblivious to the stunned silence, she elaborated.

"He was telling me about a dealer who has some

bottles to sell. I can't tell you who, or what, but these bottles are rare, world renowned, and highly desirable. If we bought six of them at £10,000 each, Ashley thinks we can easily double our money in a short while.

"Ashley has contacts around the world. He thinks he could do really well in China, of all places, but he doesn't have the money to invest."

Tara and Rick remained speechless as her mother pressed on. "But I have, of course, so I thought I may as well do something fun and exciting with it, and help Ashley to conquer the wine world. And it *is* exciting, darlings, isn't it?

"I'll be selling the house of course, to get Ashley up and running in China, but I can move in here, have the master bedroom, and we can be one big, happy family. It will be such *fun* and makes perfect sense."

"Mother, are you completely insane?"

"Honestly, Vivian, you cannot be serious?"

It appeared that, in Ashley Wilkes, Vivian had met someone as manipulative as she was.

"Look, it will be lovely. You're both out at work all day, and I'm sure I'll be just fine, pottering about, doing some gardening, and I have such plans for redecorating.

This place will look beautiful after you follow my advice. You'll have to get your own decorators in of course, because Ashley and I will need all my money for our new venture."

"No. No! NO – that is *not* going to happen, Mother. You are not coming here again unless you are invited, and I don't imagine Rick or I doing that any time soon."

"But Tara, darling, I'll have nowhere. Where else could I go?"

Tara looked her mother in the eyes,

"Frankly, Mother, I don't give a damn."

~~~

The House of the Rising Moon

Wendy Fletcher

When I first saw Timothy, he was walking briskly through the park. I noticed the neat lines of his suit, the fine cut of his hair. He walked like a gentleman. He wasn't just a stroller in the park; he was definitely heading somewhere. I liked him and noted the time.

That night I thought of him as I stood at my bedroom window, watching the rising moon.

The next day, I watched him pass again: the same walk, the same route. He was a man with a routine, punctual, reliable, trustworthy. I liked him even more and that night I dreamed of seeing him again as the growing moon hung outside my window.

On the third day, the weather let me down. Black clouds had hovered all morning. As he drew level, a crack of thunder shook the park and lightning zigzagged across the sky. I jumped clear of the tree.

I had gasped aloud and he turned. I was just a foot away. He didn't comment on my sudden appearance from behind a tree; he just asked softly 'Shall we walk back to the House together? Would you like to share my umbrella?'

I nodded, lost for words. Would I like to share his umbrella? I wanted to share his life.

'Are you enjoying the summer?' He was obviously interested in me.

'Yes, I come here most days,' I subtly prepared the ground for further accidental meetings. 'I am a nurse, you see. I work night shifts.'

He nodded and smiled at me – what a smile. He didn't ask any more questions. I expect he didn't want to sound too inquisitive but I wouldn't have minded.

I'm not exactly a proper nurse because I haven't got one of those funny upside down watches, but I would have been able to answer his questions because a lot of my friends are nurses and I have known some of them for years.

They even let me stay at the hospital sometimes when they are working there.

It was at this point I decided his name was Timothy. He looked like a Timothy when he smiled, and he was smiling again now as we huddled close under the big umbrella, hurrying toward the main entrance of the House.

Two days later, I had a chat with my best friend, Katie Graham. Katie is a social worker, and she has an office at the House. She had invited me to go and see her and as I wasn't doing anything important, I thought I might as well drop in.

She was really pleased to see me. I suppose she gets lonely in that little office. Anyway, she kept me talking for so long that I was too late to meet Timothy. Never mind, I felt sure he would understand.

I had wanted to see him though. There was some confusion to sort out. Yesterday he had walked through the park on a different path and I nearly missed him, spotting him through the trees at the last minute. We really needed to choose a special place to meet, and that night, as the moon got rounder and brighter through my window, I knew just the spot.

The evenings were long, and after we had all eaten supper at the big table I often stayed downstairs and watched television with some of my friends, but now there was so much to do. If I was going to live with Timothy, there was a lot to organise. I couldn't find my suitcase but I had a couple of old carrier bags so I stuffed as many clothes as I could into them.

This took more than one evening because my sweet little cleaning lady came each morning and couldn't seem to understand I was getting ready to move. After she had gone, all my clothes were back in the wardrobe.

I didn't see Timothy all weekend and the wait was agonising. By Monday I was so excited that I forgot to hide behind the tree and just hurtled across the grass when the nice man in the gatehouse let him in.

'Let's go to the dance tonight,' I called, forgetting to wait for him to ask me.

'I'm sorry,' he smiled that smile again, 'I already have plans for tonight.'

'Never mind.' I smiled back bravely. 'Tomorrow will be fine; we can get the bus into town.'

He nodded now and turned away but I was happy. I could wait another day and I held on to the image of that nod.

'Isn't he lovely?' A voice behind me spoke in almost a whisper, 'He's my son, you know.'

It was my dear old next-door neighbour, Agatha.

'John visits me every day in his lunch hour,' she confided, 'although he lives right across town.'

'Where does he live?' I held my breath.

She quoted the address proudly. 'It's one of those big new houses with a swimming pool in the garden.'

My excitement was bubbling now. I had never lived anywhere with a swimming pool. I even forgot to ask why she called him John – perhaps it was her pet name for him. Anyway, it didn't matter. I had an address. I could call at his house and give him a wonderful surprise.

The street lights were on as I turned the corner, so I could see there was no car in the drive, but Timothy would no doubt be back soon as there was light in the window, although the curtains were drawn.

I was pleased the moon was full now. I had tried to find a torch but my landlady was prowling around and she can be a funny old stick, insisting that the park is called the 'grounds' and demanding that we all call her 'Matron'. I didn't want her to know I was going out. She prefers us to stay in our rooms after dark – in fact she doesn't give us a choice. I knew she would be mad if she found out that I had the key the gardener lost during the summer, because she had asked us then if we had seen it and I should have said 'yes'.

Funny how she never reported it or had the lock changed. I think she had a soft spot for that gardener and didn't want to get him in trouble. He used to go up to her room on the next floor every couple of weeks and help her move that noisy old bed around.

Anyway, it had all turned out well because now I could surprise Timothy and then he could drive me back to collect my carrier bags.

I crept round to the back of the house, keeping in close by the hedge until I could see the kitchen window. There was a light here too and as I stretched my neck to see better, I caught a movement – just a shadow which flickered across the window and was gone again.

A burglar! Oh, what luck! Timothy would return and I would warn him. He would phone the police and they would arrive with sirens blaring, lights flashing. They would arrest a monster who would have brutally murdered Timothy if I had not been there. He would propose to me immediately.

Then we would go back and explain to Matron that I had to go out, and we'd show her the pictures in the paper and she would not be mad anymore and she would bring all my friends to the wedding. Oh, I love a happy ending.

Then the burglar came closer to the window and I froze. He wasn't as I imagined. He was tiny and slender. He had shoulder length hair and earrings that caught the light. He was carrying a tray of pots and he placed them in the sink below the window. I know it was the sink because I could see the taps. He had pretty eyes. He didn't look like a burglar.

In fact, he didn't look like a man. He looked more like a woman.

In fact – and my heart plummeted now – he looked just like a wife.

All this time Timothy had deceived me. He had not once mentioned having a wife.

Obviously he was planning to wait until he had got rid of her before he told me. He wouldn't have wanted me to worry – dear, kind Timothy.

I remembered how he had put his hand reassuringly on my shoulder when he postponed our date.

What a nice man.

I stared again at the window. That ugly, smug wife was still there, washing his dishes nicely, drying his dishes nicely, day after day after day. No wonder she was driving him crazy. No wonder he had decided to kill her.

Poor man, he must be terribly distressed. Poor, kind Timothy would have had to be desperate to have reached such a decision. I couldn't picture him in a violent mood. Suddenly it all fell into place. Timothy was such a gentle man. He would never have been able to go through with it.

That was why he had arranged for the gardener to leave the key where I could find it. That was why he had told his mother to give me his address. He needed me to come here tonight and do the deadly deed for him.

I rang the door- bell. The wife answered it immediately.

'Timothy asked me to come.....' I began.

'Timothy?' She echoed, 'Timothy who?'

That was the final insult. She was pretending not to know him. I pushed her aside. There was a bronze statue on the hall table.

One dull thud and she was on the floor. She lay very still but there wasn't much blood. I hope the people who came to look were not too disappointed.

They were mostly my friends. My best friends were the lovely policemen who came in their cars with sirens blaring, lights flashing. They were all dressed up special.

Then Cynthia Graham turned up and put a coat around my shoulders. I hadn't noticed how cold the night was.

Timothy came too, but he seemed a little confused by it all. He was pacing up and down, crying to the policemen, saying he didn't understand it, he had only met me a few times when he was visiting his mother.

Then a policeman asked me to go for a ride in his car. He was very handsome and looked quite distinguished in his blue uniform so I said I would. This made Timothy really jealous. As we were leaving, he screamed at me that I was wicked, and that his sister had been a wonderful woman.

Now I was confused. I didn't even know he had a sister. Fancy him worrying about his relatives at a time like this when we could look forward to our whole future together.

~~~

SETTING THE SCENE

Scene-setting prompts were chosen from a selection.

...

Drifting Apart

Jan Cunningham

The two men were complete opposites: Sonny calm, laid back, come-day-go-day-devil-take-Sunday, whereas Jack was the worrier always fearing the worst.

They worked the fishing boat together and made a fair living over the years. Both married local girls and while Sonny's wife, Susan, was busy having babies, Jenny – Jack's wife – took an accounting course at the college in the nearby town, since she wasn't as lucky in the baby department. She took over the account books and kept a tight rein on them, which meant they weren't rich but managed well enough and were content with their lot.

Then, a few years later and quite out of the blue, Jenny gave birth to a baby girl. She was the apple of her parents' eyes, especially as Jenny had been told there would be no more.

As time marched on and their families grew up, both Sonny and Jack were looking forward to having a bit more free time. Daniel, Sonny's eldest son, was now working on the boat with them, and his second son, Jimmy, was showing interest too.

"Wouldn't it be grand to hand over to the boys in a few years time and sit back and reap the benefit of our labours," said Sonny one evening while sitting in the pub, nursing a pint.

"You'd be bored out of your mind, and you'd miss going out to sea too much," answered Jack.

"Aye, mebbe, but it's a nice dream," said Sonny as he watched the news on the pub's TV.

Back at Jack's house, the scene was anything but peaceful. Jenny was holding her daughter in her arms, making soothing noises and trying not to cry herself. Amy had just told her mum she was pregnant.

Dear God, thought Jenny. Sixteen years old and her future gone.

"Who's the father, Amy?" asked Jenny with her fingers crossed behind her daughter's back. She had heard through gossip that Amy had been seen out and about with a lad from the nearby town, known locally as "the leader of the pack". I'll kill him, swore Jenny to herself, or Jack will when he knows. But Amy wouldn't answer; she just cried all the harder.

"OK, Love, we'll leave that for now. How far gone are you?"

"Twelve weeks."

"Good God, why didn't you come to me sooner?"

"'Cos I tried to ignore it, hoped it would go away. I was scared of what Dad would say. If I can't go to college he'll be so disappointed. I just can't face him."

"OK, but have you thought about what you are going to do about your situation?" said Jenny gently.

"Oh Mum, I don't know," wailed Amy. "But please, Mum, don't tell Dad just yet. Please, Mum, please," she begged.

"Not right this minute, no, but he'll have to know sooner or later."

"Not if I don't keep it," replied Amy stonily.

Jenny was shocked that her first thought was, please don't kill my first grandchild. But she kept her thoughts to herself and said out loud, "Whatever your decision, I will stand by you."

And she meant it. It was her daughter's future at stake, not hers.

"Well love, you get off to bed before your dad gets back, and we'll sort it out in the morning."

When Jack returned from the pub, Jenny kept her promise not to tell him about his daughter's pregnancy, but it was hard.

As it happened, he wouldn't have listened anyway because he was up in arms about the item he had seen on the news on the pub's TV, reporting that the EU was going to ban all drift fishing on the first of January 2015.

"They can't do it, Jen! They can't just ban *all* drift fishing. They can't be allowed to," he raged. "You do realise what it means for us? We'll be finished. No boat, no fishing, no income, and what will Sonny and I do? We're in our fifties, and all we've ever known is fishing. Who's gonna retrain us at our age, and for what? No, we have to fight this, somehow."

From then on, Jack was as a man driven. He held meetings with the local fishermen, wrote passionately on a blog he set up, and went to meetings in Plymouth to hear what the National Federation of Fishermens' Organisations (NFFO) proposed.

Sonny, of course, took the opposite view – that the EU couldn't just ban outright without consultations, and in his eyes it would never happen.

Jenny tried and tried to talk to Jack about Amy over the forthcoming weeks, but he was so wrapped up in the campaign she couldn't get through to him. It was "Just a minute, Jen, I have to take this call," or "Hang on, Jen, just got to put this on my blog while it's fresh in my mind," or "Can it wait? I've got to go out."

Amy decided to keep the baby, despite its father (yes, it was who Jenny had guessed) saying that if she didn't have an abortion she would be on her own as he was far too young to be saddled. Jenny was worried sick that Jack would realise his daughter was pregnant as she got bigger and be so angry with her... but his only comment was a sarcastic, "Our Amy's put on a bit of weight. What she doing? Eating for two? Ha-ha."

The weeks flew past.

Jenny made sure her daughter did all the right things – attending anti-natal classes, seeing the midwife regularly – and booked her into hospital for the delivery. She always went with her and could have cried when she saw the scans of their grandchild, but still she couldn't find the right time or the words to tell Jack. He was so wrapped up in his fight to save the drift fishing world that he never listened, or heard anything she said.

"I swear to God, Sue," moaned Jenny to Sonny's wife, "if I walked round naked and served up puppy pie he wouldn't notice or care these days. He's like a man possessed. Talk about tunnel vision – he's got it in spades."

"Do you want Sonny to have a word? See if he can get through? I mean, Amy's six months gone. You're lucky she's not very big."

"*No*, no. Thanks, Sue, but I must be the one to tell him – and I will. I will, I promise you. Soon."

One evening, when Jack returned from another of his endless meetings in Plymouth, he came rushing in, picked Jenny up and swung her round in his arms.

"We've done it, Jen! We've bloody gone and done it! The first week in June we are sending a flotilla of all the fishing boats from round here, plus picking up others as we go, and we're going to travel up the Thames to London to protest loud and long about the ban. How about that then, Jen? You never believed this would happen, did you? But it is, Jen, it really is!"

Well, that was that. All Jack talked about from then on was the planning of the flotilla: how many of the local fishermen would back them, where it would start from, how many other boats would join them as they made their way round the south coast to the start of the Thames estuary.

The trip would take three to four days, there and back, and that meant making sure there were enough provisions, clothing, fuel, etc on board.

Needless to say, neither Sonny nor his son would be joining them.

As Sonny said, dismissively, "The whole idea is daft. They've got negotiators in the government to sort it out. What do think we pay 'em for?"

"Yes, I know. That's why we need to be there and show a united front to make sure they understand our worries. The ban, as it stands, is unnecessary, heavy-handed, disproportionate and inappropriate for our UK waters, and we have to ram that down our negotiators throats," Jack said fervently.

Amy, meantime, was keeping well out of her dad's way: not coming down till Jack had left, eating her dinner before he got home and either going to Sue's –

whose family were sworn to silence – or spending her evenings in her room, watching TV or playing on her computer.

She was worried sick: frightened of what would happen when Dad finally found out and terrified of the coming birth. Mum had tried to explain what would happen gently, but it sounded awful.

As the first of June drew near, Jack's behaviour became even more frenetic: checking and rechecking the boat, making sure he had everything he thought he might need and meeting frequently with the other fisherman who had agreed to be in the flotilla to make doubly sure everyone knew what to do. They were to set sail at high tide on the twenty-seventh of June.

And they did. The weather forecast was good and most of the villagers turned out to wave and cheer them on.

It was a magnificent sight: the harbour full of boats of all shapes, sizes, colours... some with sails up, and all decked out with Union Jacks. The lead boat sounded its hooter and they were off, bobbing up and down, moving slowly out to sea.

Amy could now relax for a few days while her Dad was safely at sea. Her small heart-shaped face was pale and drawn; her usually merry dark brown eyes were dull. She was generally listless and tired. As her bump was not overly big she had managed to hide it well under long smock-tops and shirts.

Once the flotilla was under way, it was reported in the local news and then the national television news, with daily bulletins on its progress.

One night, Jenny called up to Amy, "Come and look at the Tele, Ames. You can see your dad on his boat. Hurry up or you'll miss him!"

When Amy didn't appear, Jenny turned to see her daughter clinging to the bannister at the bottom of the stairs, white-faced and doubled over with pain.

"Mum," she cried, "I think it's coming."

"It can't be," moaned Jenny. "You're not due for another three weeks."

"Do something, Mum, please. I'm in agony."

And with that, Amy slumped to the floor. Jenny noticed fluid and then blood on the carpet. "Oh my God," she whispered.

"Ambulance *now*. Jenny, come on – move!"

The next few hours passed in a haze of blue lights flashing, white Doctors' coats, nurses rushing about, and then a calm male voice said, "Theatre, *now*."

Jenny stood paralysed in the corridor with shock and fear for her daughter's life. No one seemed to notice her – they were all too busy with Amy. After what felt like a lifetime, but was probably closer to half an hour, Jenny heard a voice saying, "Are you Amy's mother?"

She spun round to see a Doctor in theatre greens.

"Yes, I am. Please, Doctor, is she alright?"

He gave her a wide smile and said, "She'll be fine, and you have a beautiful baby granddaughter. Amy's still asleep from the anaesthetic, but you can sit with her as soon as she is back in the ward."

"Thank you. Thank you so much, but what happened? She wasn't due for another three weeks."

"Amy had a placental abruption, which is when the placenta comes away from the wall of the uterus and can be very dangerous to her and the little one. Fortunately, you got her here quickly, and we were able to deliver the baby straightaway by caesarean section. As to why it happens, no one really knows, but as long as it is dealt with quickly, all is well."

Later, as Jenny sat by her daughter's bedside, gazing at her new, precious granddaughter, she wondered how on earth she was going to break the news to Jack. He was due back any time now. What a mess.

The protest had gone better than expected. When they moored up at Tower Bridge, a crowd gathered to watch the boats with their Union Jack flags and protest banners dancing in the breeze. They waved and cheered them on.

Later that day, NFFO officials had a meeting with the government department that would be negotiating with the EU on behalf of Britain's fishing industry.

Afterwards, the NFFO officials felt they had made their points clearly and succinctly to the Department for Environment, Food and Rural Affairs. They had been given assurances that all that could be done to get the best deal for drift fishermen, would be done.

On his way home, high on hope and enthusiasm, Jack tried again to speak to Jenny. He wanted to tell her all about it but, for some reason, he'd only got her answer-phone for the last couple of days. Hope she and Amy are alright, he thought. Must be, or she would have phoned me. Don't matter I'll be home soon.

When Jack arrived home that evening, there were no lights on. That's odd, he thought. Where the devil are they? They knew I was due back today.

He didn't expect a welcoming committee, but a hug and a hot meal would have been nice.

He went into the kitchen where he saw a note on the table saying, "Jack, when you get in, please come to hospital. Don't worry, it's not bad news."

His stomach clenching with fear, he ran out of the house, jumped in his car and raced to the hospital. When he asked where his wife and daughter were, a nurse took him to the maternity wing.

His mind was in turmoil. Jenny couldn't have an unexpected baby, could she? No. Then it must be Amy. Oh please, God, let her be alright. The whys and wherefores could come later; just let her be OK.

Jenny came out to meet him in the corridor.

"I know, I know," she said. "I should have told you a long time ago and I'm sorry, but you were so caught up in your campaign I just couldn't get through to you."

"Oh, Jen, it's me that should be sorry. You poor loves, having to go through this on your own. Tell me what happened."

And Jenny did.

"Now," she said with a smile, "come and say hello to Faith, your granddaughter. Amy chose that name because she thought that's what we've all got to have now for our futures. Faith that whatever happens we'll manage."

Weeks later, Jack and Sonny were out on an early tide, listening to the creaks of the old boat and searching for gulls to show them where to cast their nets.

Jack turned to Sonny and said, "This has been a helluva year hasn't it?"

Sonny nodded agreement. "But with a bit of luck and a good strong back wind we'll get there, won't we?"

"Aye, and with a little faith as well," said Sonny with a broad grin and his blue eyes twinkling.

~~~

The Reaper

Val Chapman

The four friends made their way to the park.

Taking advantage of the warm, late summer afternoon, they had hurriedly put together a picnic, and were looking forward to one of their last trips out together before school started again.

While Anne and Georgia set out the picnic, Julian and Dick stood watching another boy from the village having fun on the slide. Timmy was not much younger than they were, and with his large blue eyes and ready grin, was a delight to be around. He came bounding over to them, and the girls promised to save him some biscuits, before he ran back to the playground.

'Should Timmy really be out on his own?' wondered Julian. 'I heard Dad say he had been assessed, and has a mental age of 5.'

The girls paused and sat back on their heels to watch Timmy taking turns on the slide with the younger children.

'Oh, you know Timmy, he'll be fine.' Anne dismissed his concerns.

'Besides, we're here now, to keep an eye on him,' countered George. 'And it's so quiet and dull around here, nothing's likely to happen anyway.

'Now, give us a hand with this picnic. Just because we're girls, it doesn't mean we have to do all this kind of stuff. Boys are nearly as capable as us you know!'
'Oooh, alright, Georgia, miss bossy-boots.' Dick laughed, and finished taking the drinks and crisps from the bag.

The little group had known each other all their lives, living close to each other in the village. At thirteen, George was the eldest. Julian was a few months younger, while Dick and Anne were both twelve.

From time to time, Timmy ran across to them for food. Before long, there was very little left to eat or drink. Clouds had started to gather overhead and the friends decided to set off for home.

'Has Timmy gone already?'

'Well, he was at the playground a minute ago'. Julian, true to character, had been keeping any eye on the little boy.

'His Aunty Ruth probably came to get him. He often goes to her house round about this time'.

They packed up their picnic and headed out of the park, scanning the area for signs of Timmy as they went. They were still laughing together as they crossed the road leading to the picturesque village they all called home.

Suddenly, the peace of the afternoon was shattered by squealing brakes, and a loud bang. An eerie silence settled along the street.

The friends stopped in their tracks and Anne screamed.

'TIMMY. Oh my God, Timmy!'

They dropped everything they were carrying and ran to the scene, just metres away.

The driver of the car was already crouched beside Timmy. Some villagers who had heard the crash appeared, but it was obvious to everyone there was nothing they could do to help Timmy.

Amid all the noise and lights of ambulances, police sirens, and the gathered crowds, George noticed a strange, unfamiliar figure. He – she could see the figure was a 'he' – was standing quite still, looking down at Timmy's lifeless body.

Standing beside the figure and holding his hand, was Timmy.

The figure looked down at this Timmy and smiled. George could clearly see their friend smile back as they walked hand in hand along the road.

It was at that moment, seeing the apparition's beautiful smile, that George fell in love.

She wasn't stupid. She guessed the figure was the 'Grim Reaper', but to her he was an angel, and she couldn't stop thinking about him.

The children did what children do and grew up – all except poor Timmy of course – and, although they remained close, went their separate ways. George was the only one who couldn't seem to settle, flitting from one job to the next, one relationship to the next, always on the lookout for something better.

When George witnessed another accidental death, this time a poor little old lady choking on a scone in the tea shop, the Reaper appeared again. She was aware it wasn't normal to see the Grim Reaper – not for the living anyway – and that, in itself, proved to George that they had a special connection.

Once again, the mysterious figure didn't stay around for long. He simply smiled reassuringly and walked off, guiding the old lady along the road towards the light.

George, despite her efforts not to, fell deeper and deeper for the apparition, and knew without a doubt, that her destiny was to be with him. She vowed to find a way for them to be together.

It took a while to formulate her plan, but once in place, there was no going back.

It wasn't easy choosing her first victim, but they say the first murder is the hardest and that proved to be the case for George. She knew they would see each other at the point of death and it was up to her to orchestrate these meetings.

Each time, George positioned herself in a spot where she could see her beloved and he could see her, but without arousing suspicion. Those moments drove her on as she became more and more desperate to see him.

She was onto her sixth murder now, each chosen to be different, with nothing to link her to any of them. She had become perversely proud of her achievements.

The trouble was, the time she could spend with him was fleeting, and George knew she wanted more.

Her Reaper had gazed lovingly and reassuringly at her victims, gently leading them to their next destination. They had spent far more time, and had far more contact with him than she had. She needed to find a way they could be together for longer.

She worked out a way they could be together for much longer. As her plan evolved, she was confident he would soon see that she would make him as happy as he made her. She also realised she was bound to get caught sooner or later, so she decided to put her new plan into action before it was too late.

George wasn't the slightest bit worried on the day she decided to kill herself.

She had toyed with the idea of jumping off a nearby bridge but reasoned that it would probably leave her in a bit of a mess, and she wanted to look nice when he came for her.

She had written down details of all of her past misdemeanours; it seemed the right thing to do. She did feel a little sorry for her victim's families, but sometimes she had to put her needs first.

She wore the new dress she had bought specially for the occasion. After arranging the pills beside her, she opened a bottle of red wine.

The next time George opened her eyes, it was to see the now familiar figure of a Reaper standing beside her.

She smiled as she gazed up at him.

Her smile vanished as she realised he was not 'her' Reaper – the one she had spent most of her adult life longing to be with.

Where was he? What was going on?

'Who are you? Where is MY Reaper?

'He should be here – I want HIM.

'I need to see HIM.'

The figure looked down at her.

'Dear me, I've never encountered anyone so demanding.

'Oh Georgia, you should have realised there is more than just one Reaper. The one you have been aching to see is one of the Good Reapers, for good people.

'After all your exploits, I hardly think you qualify to be collected by a Good Reaper, do you?

'You, my dear, will be coming with me, and you certainly won't be meeting any Good Reapers where we will be going.'

Red eyes and yellow, pointed teeth smiled at George – not at all lovingly.

~~~

A Dress for a Princess

Wendy Fletcher

I am hot and tired, and I know that I shouldn't have put off this trip to the shops until the last minute but that seems to have become my style in the past few months.

Shopping with a toddler is testing reserves I didn't know I had, and I fear that they will run out at any moment.

The assistants have smiled and been polite but I am left with the impression they would have preferred us to shop elsewhere. We have asked for more than they can offer and they have done their best to accommodate us, but it is an uneasy compromise.

Pushing these thoughts out of the way to deal with later, I turn back to Alicia. She is excited about this afternoon's party and giggles as I try awkwardly to zip her into a frothy pink dress.

I try to stay calm and not dampen her enthusiasm but I am struggling. It has been another long day in an unbelievably long year.

She is almost three now, and every day brings more exciting discoveries for her and more unforeseen challenges for me. We have fought through sleepless nights when her screams reached neighbouring houses and morning has found us huddled under a duvet, too exhausted to face the day. We have travelled together the precarious road of frustration that leads to potty training.

This term she has started nursery and made her first friends outside the family. I have watched her growing more independent and my heart has been torn. Part of me is delighted that she is developing into a relatively normal child. Part of me wants to keep her safely cocooned against my shoulder, the unknowing baby who won't have to field awkward questions and face life's cruel realities.

It was at nursery that she met the new little friend who has invited her to the birthday party this afternoon, and my thoughts return to the dress. The length is about right but she still has that chubby layer of baby fat on her torso and the stitching pulls tight across the chest. I try to stop her bouncing long enough to check if the label corresponds with the ticket on the coat-hanger. It does but I am still not convinced. 'Age two to three' sounds quite vague now. Does this mean that all children of two and three conform to this standard?

Evidently not. Mine is definitely stretching the boundaries. I thought we were coming out of the phase where she pushed away all my culinary efforts despite much persuasion. Now I wonder if I have been over-feeding her. Is she on the slippery slope to a bad diet?

Another problem to examine later, but right now I have to deal with the reality that I have picked up the wrong size for my child. She is almost three so perhaps it is time to look at 'Age three to four'. Such a silly, trivial mistake but I am cross with myself. It means that I have to get her out of the dress again and clothed in her own little skirt and jumper, complete with tights and boots.

Whoever invented lace-up boots for toddlers?

Then we will have to trail back across the shop floor to the rail and only hope that it comes in a bigger size. If I could properly explain this to her, it would be easier but her vocabulary is limited. At this moment it is limited to 'Princess, 'licia be princess'.

I cannot make her understand that we will get another dress, the same but bigger – hopefully. She resists in the only way she knows: by making the removal of the garment as difficult as possible. She wriggles and protests as she is buttoned back into her own clothes, pushing away my hands and wrapping determined little fingers around my wrists. I know the thought she cannot express is that the beautiful pink dress with its shimmering decorations is about to disappear from her life. She is disappointed and I hate to see disappointment in her soft hazel eyes, now clouded with tears.

The most hurtful part is that it's not about the dress. It's about me. She is disappointed that I have offered her something and then taken it away again. She is even more disappointed that I have not heeded her pleas and, for just a moment, I am tempted to put the dress back on her and let her walk proudly out of the shop, but I know I mustn't.

I must find a way of coping with emotions I see in her eyes. I will see more disappointment. I will see hurt and pain and anguish. I have to learn to deal with those looks of confusion, bewilderment and a sense of injustice. I have to mop up the stream of tears that gush forth and hold back my own until the day comes when we might cry together and mourn the loss of her mother.

Only then – maybe – will we be able to find some humour in our lives again, and perhaps laugh about the day we went shopping for her first party dress and had to clamber into a tiny, unlit storage area beyond a mountain of boxes waiting to be unpacked, because there were changing rooms for ladies and girls, and changing rooms for men and boys, but we didn't fit into their percieved vision of a family. We were just a lost little girl and a bereaved Dad, trying to find our way to some kind of normality.

~~~

In the Laundry

Cathy Cade

The muffled rumblings behind the door became a clattering cacophony when it opened, releasing the smell of bleach and wet washing. Inside the basement, a single light bulb threw shadows, which danced when the door slammed.

The washing machines hammered and hissed, but at floor level things were less steamy. Between the machines, something small and round shifted in the darkness.

Maxie Mouse turned to the long-lashed companion behind him.

'We'll be all right here.'

A washing machine gurgled.

The mouse with the big eyes twitched her whiskers.

'Are you sure, Max?'

'That cat can't get down here. The basement door's always shut in the daytime to keep in the noise.'

Strutting to a hole in the skirting board, he whipped out two tiny chairs followed by a bistro table – which was almost as big as the hole. With a flourish, the table was laid, the candle lit.

Misty Mouse sat.

Max produced a large wedge of cheese and proceeded to carve.

Among the overhead clatter, the basement door opened and closed again. Max tiptoed between the washing machines to confirm the sturdy wrinkle-clad legs descending the wooden stairs were those of Bessie, the laundry-maid. She hummed to herself as she emptied the big top-loading machine and filled it again from another laundry basket. The open lid of the machine trembled above her as the smaller front-loader beside it began a spin cycle.

Reassured, Max returned to Misty. Above their table, water gurgled through a hose to fill the machine. He put a hand to one silky ear.

'I hear a distant waterfall.'

She giggled. 'You're such a romantic, Max.'

A drip landed on the floor nearby. Another followed, splashing Misty. Above them, a connector on the big machine was seeping.

Max moved the table further away and, with a bow, invited Miss Misty to sit again. So they didn't notice the drips falling faster nor the puddle that formed, to creep under the washer.

Bessie emptied the front-loader, humming her favourite hymn as she folded the clean laundry into a basket. The thin cotton was almost dry after its spin; she took it to the ironing press, which hiccupped puffs of steam. She instinctively avoided them as she brought the press down on a pillowcase to test the temperature. Steam billowed, reaching out for anything within range, but Bessie had moved to adjust the dial. As she turned away, the dial seemed to stick its tongue out – an old trick of the shadows. The pillowcase was now flat and dry, and the beast had run out of steam.

She loaded the washer again and went to retrieve the washing powder from the top-loader. Her slippers met water spreading from under the machine. It soaked through the thin soles to her toes. She investigated behind the machine and found water dribbling down a hose, to pool on the floor. Amos would have to come and fix it.

Something moved.

On the floor, pink eyes gleamed in the semi-darkness.

Bessie's scream reverberated around the basement as she pounded up the stairs.

The echoes had faded when the a damp slipper propelled a large black cat down the stairs. The door slammed behind it.

Max had been scurrying to pack away his table and chairs. Misty tried to help but, in her panic, she pushed the table into the mouse-hole at the wrong angle, and it wedged tight. They turned, to see green eyes searching the darkness.

Satan, the cat, slunk between the washing machines, to be drenched by the spray now spurting from the hose above. As he shook water from his fur, the mice scattered.

Misty ran out across the floor. The door to the front-loader was open so she jumped in.

Max scaled the big top-loader. Satan leapt after him, landing on a switch. The vibrating machine began to shake, knocking over the box of washing powder, which spilled to the floor.

Max leapt to the lower machine. He skittered down it to the ground while Satan skidded along the top and tumbled over the edge. Picking himself up, the cat spied Max by the steam press and sprang, knocking the door of the front-loader shut as he passed. The bigger machine was now shuddering, its loosened connector gushing water.

Max scaled the steam press and ran across to its handle, which lowered under his weight. The top pressing plate descended.

The resulting cloud of steam emitted an unearthly screech – like the wail of a broken fiddle. When it cleared, Satan hung by his tail from the steam press.

Max slithered down the handle and dropped, allowing the handle to rise again and release Satan. Dumped onto the floor, the cat drummed his fingers and waved his flattened tail in fury, while Max rocked with laughter.

Still steaming, Satan shook himself from head to tail – restoring its snake-like roundness – and pounced.

Max scuttled up the big machine's hose, but before he reached the top it fell away, sending Max leaping for the nearest shelf. He scampered up to a higher one where he could watch the bubbles rising from the drenched washing powder.

The door at the top of the stairs opened.

'You caught them meeces yet?'

This was followed by a shriek. 'What you gone an' done now, you useless cat?' The door slammed.

When it re-opened, trousered legs in rubber boots clumped down the stairs and waded to a row of taps on the wall beneath the shelves. Amos turned one and the cascade stopped.

Bessie – also booted – bustled down the stairs to turn off the big machine. She handed Amos a broom. He swept the suds toward a drain, but Bessie's broom was mostly aimed at Satan.

Amos left, dragging the bedraggled cat with him, Bessie's eyes moved nervously from side to side.

'I sure hope them meeces drowned in that flood.'

Nobody replied.

Taking a fresh pack of washing powder from the shelf, she poured some into a drawer on the front-loader, and pressed a button to start the wash. This time she returned the box of powder to its shelf behind the machines.

Max tried to keep out of sight as he searched for Misty. Staying close to the machines, he looked under them and down the corridors between them. He turned to begin again and stopped.

Pressed against the clear round door of the front-loader, Misty rotated slowly as the water level rose. Behind her, folds of laundry shaped a shadowy smile.

Max ran into the middle of the floor. Jumping up and down, he pointed to the door of the machine.

Something squeaked. Bessie leaped onto a stool.

In front of the washing machine, a mouse was having some kind of fit.

Perhaps it would die. She grabbed an unopened box from the shelf behind her and threw.

It missed. The mouse ran up to the top of the machine and sat up, as if taunting her.

She reached for a broom. With both hands, she brought it down – then clutched at the shelf behind her as the stool wobbled. Once steady again, she searched in vain for flattened fur.

The machine had stopped filling; her blow had caught the off-switch.

She couldn't suppress another shriek when the mouse reappeared further along the machine's top.

It *was* taunting her!

Angry now, she raised the broom for another blow, but the creature leapt aside and her broom hit another button. The door of the front-loader popped open, spewing out water and soggy laundry.

The pile of wet washing on the floor moved.

Bessie's eyes closed as she screamed, so she didn't see Misty emerge from the pile and run to the mouse-hole, where Max joined her. Together, they tugged at the wood blocking the hole until it moved, and the pair disappeared into the wall.

The machines waited.

Bessie heard the scrabbling behind the wall and told herself the mouse had gone.

'Washin don' move by hisself. That washin just moved cos the water were drainin out of it.'

The sound of her own voice reassured her.

'Better get them wet things sorted, afore they get to smelling.'

She stepped off the stool, using the broom still clutched in her fist to steady herself.

She wasn't accustomed to silence in the laundry. She started to sing the hymn about those in peril, but her voice sounded eerie, wobbling in the stillness.

She went to re-set the steam press. It spat at her before subsiding to a grumble as the fresh water heated.

She pressed a button to drain the top-loader. While it pumped, she scooped the wet washing from the floor back into the front-loader, which coughed when she turned it on. Soon it was chuntering resentfully as it filled and turned.

The big top-loader beeped angrily to tell her it had finished emptying.

She mocked her own nervousness. Amos would be back as soon as he'd found another connector for the water hose, but she wouldn't wait all day for that lazy good-for-nothing. The smaller front-loader would take the rest in two batches. She raised the lid of the top-loader.

The wet sheets inside were heavy and resisted her tug. She stretched to reach the last bedsheet at the bottom.

Max had returned to retrieve his uneaten cheese; he had found fresh breadcrumbs in the pantry that would go well with it. But the cheese was nowhere in sight.

Machines were grinding and grumbling; Bessie had them working again. Had she tidied up his cheese?

He found her reaching into the big top-loading washing machine with one foot off the ground. The other was on tiptoe.

It left the floor.

The machine rumbled.

Both feet flew up, out of sight. The lid crashed.

A hollow belch echoed off the walls of the basement.

~~~

Changeling

Stephen Oliver

Of all the rooms in the beautiful old house, this was the most elegant.

It was large and light with south-facing windows. With midwinter fast approaching, evergreens decorated the huge fireplace, lamp sconces and picture frames. Wonderful paintings hung on the walls. Delicate glass and porcelain figurines stood on tables that separated shelves on the walls from one another. Marquetry, small statues, cameos, and other items of beauty and elegance adorned those self-same shelves.

Chairs and a sofa were of similar quality and value as well as being comfortable to sit on. This was the room of a wealthy family that loved both its possessions and its comfort.

Despite the grace and comfort of the room, Eleanor McKenzie had never felt comfortable in it. She never felt comfortable in any room of the house, despite being heir to both house and surrounding lands. Her father, the Honourable Nigel McKenzie, was the 37th Viscount McKenzie, in an unbroken family line going back close on a thousand years. And she was due to inherit when he shuffled off his mortal coil.

Eleanor gazed out of the windows at the leaden grey sky with its wintry clouds scudding above the naked trees. Something inside her yearned to be out in that chilly weather, dancing with the wind and the few remaining leaves as they blew down from their branches – free to do whatever she wished.

And yet, duty called, even as she sat here and gazed wistfully.

"Damn duty," she muttered. "And damn that stupid gamekeeper. Why on earth did he have to catch me like that? I thought he was on the other side of the estate."

She had been walking through the woods the day before, as was her wont, when she felt a sudden desire to remove all her clothes and dance naked through the trees.

The gamekeeper had found her as she was undoing her blouse, her anorak and jumper abandoned on the leaves at her feet.

He had made her re-dress herself before bundling her back to the house. He had then had a private word with her father, who was lying in bed with medical monitors surrounding him on all sides. Her father had summoned her shortly afterwards and forbidden her to leave the house. He then informed her that her duty was to ease the transition of their property when he died, and that she should speak with the family lawyer at once.

She was delighted when she discovered that the man would not be able to come until the following day – and then not until late afternoon.

And so, she found herself sitting in the old salon, staring out of the window and wishing she were somebody else.

Anybody else.

In the background, outside the firmly closed and locked door, she could hear the servants bustling up and down the corridor, preparing for this evening's party.

One of her father's suggestions was that she should spend more time in discourse with others of her social stratum. She much preferred to be on her own and felt that she had not been born for this life.

She stood up and walked to the fireplace. Her fingers reached out and fondled the holly leaves and berries. Even now, she could sense the life within them as it slowly ebbed away in the heat. A life that felt closer to her own than the rest of the room.

Moving away from the heat of the fire, she found herself walking around the room in anticlockwise circles, around and around and around. Again and again, she passed the books and paintings, the chairs and tables as she spiralled slowly outwards. Each circuit brought her a little closer to the long windows in the wall, and the small secret door between them.

Even to herself, she could not admit what she was about to do, although in her heart of hearts she had already reached the decision.

Finally, she stood with her fingers on the concealed door handle, digging out the duplicate key she'd had made months before.

Still pretending to herself that she was doing no more than going for a breath of fresh air, she unlocked the door.

As soon as it was open, she slipped outside into the raw wind and icy cold and locked the door behind her.

Free!

As far as everyone else knew, she was still in the salon, waiting for the family solicitor to arrive.

She took a deep breath and revelled in the chilly rush of air to her lungs, which somehow stopped the rest of her body from shivering.

This was where she belonged: out in the wild world, not inside that stuffy building. She felt gratitude for those comforts that her father had given her, but nowhere in her heart could she find the slightest feeling of love for him. There was less emotional bond between them than a man would feel for an old pair of boots, thrown away because they have outlived their usefulness.

She skipped lightly along the patio, passing the darkened library and her father's study. A quick look into the lighted dining room showed that nobody was present, so she dashed past and around the corner. The windows on this side of the house all had their curtains drawn; no-one would spot her going past them.

It took a little longer for her to negotiate the ornamental garden to reach the wall surrounding the entire estate. Another duplicate key enabled her to slip through the little gate and out into the woodland beyond: the same woodland that interfering gamekeeper had found her wandering in only yesterday.

She rambled among trees and bushes, touching the occasional branch and kicking leaves up into the air. Although her motions seemed random, she soon discerned her meanderings were taking her in a specific direction. Once she was sure of where she was heading, she began to hurry – through the trees towards the centre of the woods.

Something inside told her she would find everything there that she truly wanted.

The last trees parted before her as she came to the place the local people called the Fairy Dell.

She remembered the wonderful days she had spent there with her mother when she was a little girl. They would sit together on the grass, making daisy chains and crowns of flowers. In autumn, they ate the berries that grew in the bushes surrounding the glade. Her mother always told her enchanting stories, saying that this was a magical place: one where, if she wished hard enough, all her dreams would come true.

Then came the terrible day when her mother fell ill. Doctors had no idea what ailed her, but it was as if all the vitality was being leached from her.

What made it worse for Eleanor was that she was approaching puberty, and there was no woman in her life to guide her through it, although Mrs Cullen, the housekeeper, did her best to explain everything in her gruff way.

One morning, her father told her that her mother had died during the night. She never saw her again. The coffin was closed during the funeral, and she was buried with almost indecent haste in the family crypt.

With her mother's death, her father withdrew from her, and she was left to grow up alone. Eventually, he remarried. Her stepmother was a kind and loving woman, but Eleanor was unable to connect with her emotionally or with the half-siblings that came along later.

As she came to the dell, she felt, in some strange way, as if she was coming home.

The place was different.

There were tents everywhere, as if some spectral pageant were taking place.

The clearing was like a chiaroscuro painting, colourless in the grey afternoon. Eleanor wandered among the tents, peering into them and seeking those who had erected them. Nowhere was a single living being to be found. It was as if everything had been abandoned, to fade away and vanish with the morning mist.

She started to despair, as if she had perhaps missed her chance and would never be able to find her true place in this world. Or any other.She sat outside the largest tent and began to cry.

Misery so clouded her senses that she did not hear the approach of the young man. Or perhaps he had appeared out of nowhere.

"Who weeps here among the tents of the Fair Folk?" he asked in a light and musical voice. "Are you one that regrets their passing back to their own world, or do you seek to travel with them?"

Eleanor looked up and saw him standing close to her, a wry smile on his thin lips, the skin wrinkling around his violet, almond-shaped eyes. His hair was as white as birch bark, brushed back but unable to conceal the pointed tips of his ears.

"Who are you?" she asked.

"One who himself has just arrived here, well-nigh too late to make my own return." He reached down to help her stand and looked deep into her eyes.

"Ah, now I understand what you seek here. This world," – a wave of his arm included everything outside the dell – "is no more yours than it is mine.

Come with me, and I shall show you wonders that this mundane reality could never hope to equal."

She stared at him in wonder before looking around at the tents. "Will you take me with you?"

"If you so desire."

"Then it is my heartfelt wish to leave here forever."

With a wave of his hand, everything around them changed. The drab tents were replaced by bright golds and deep reds; shining blues and brilliant greens. In the same instant, people appeared, hurrying among the tents, talking and singing; laughing and joking.

Eleonora gasped. "Who are all these?"

"Why, who else but the Fair Folk? Your folk, the Fey."

"What do you mean?"

"It takes but one look to know that you are Feykin yourself, a Half-Fairy. You would never have found the tents were you not."

"But... But... But I cannot be. My father is Viscount McKenzie, descendant of a long line." She would have gone on, but the young man laid a finger over her lips.

"And who, do you think, was your mother?"

Before she could answer, a voice shrieked above the hubbub surrounding them.

"Eleanor, my child. You have found your way home! I am so glad to see you." She turned around and beheld her mother – the one person she had thought she would never see again.

"I don't understand anything." She sobbed as her mother embraced her.

"I am one of the Fey," her mother told her. "I wandered from the tents one day, met your father, and fell in love with him. But the Fey cannot live long in the world of the mundane. I sickened and had to return to my own world before I died.

"He forbade me from taking you with me, but now it is your choice. You can stay with me forever."

She linked her arm through Eleanor's and led her from the tents into their own, true world.

~~~

The disappearance of the eldest child of the 37th Viscount McKenzie is one of the enduring mysteries of our time. She vanished from a room she had locked herself into in the family home, and no-one has seen her since.

Agnes

George Holmes

Ted, waking early, looked at the slumbering Tracy. He got up and made mugs of tea for them both.

Tracy was awake when he returned. She had borrowed one of his shirts and wasn't wearing anything else.

"I've made you a cuppa it's not sugared, I can get some sugar if you like it with."

"Thanks it's okay I don't take sugar."

Tracy was sitting up in the bed leaning back against the headboard. She had picked up a travel brochure from the bedside cabinet and flicked through it.

Tracy barely occupied the sweatshirt; it was big on her. Agnes would have overflowed it. When she moved, her swaying breasts would have stirred the material like waves on the sea. It would have only half-covered her ample bottom.

He missed her terribly.

He had met Tracy at Wilkinson's Meat Pie and Mash Emporium, bumping into her whilst collecting his steak and porter pie (large portion) with extra gravy, peas and carrots. As her meal was knocked from her hands, he felt duty-bound to replace it. They made their way to a corner table and ate together companionably.

After the meal, Ted had invited Tracy for a drink at his local pub, the Wellington Walrus. He couldn't remember how many pints of Really Quite Peculiar Bitter had been consumed but it probably ran into double figures. Tracy had stuck to half pints of brown ale, delicately dunking her pork scratchings in the froth.

Tracy looked up from the brochures. "What's the attraction with Great Yarmouth then?"

"Well, I've been to Blackpool, Scarborough Filey, Bridlington – oh, and Skegness – so I thought I would try somewhere a bit more exotic, and warmer."

Ted Crouch was Marketing Manager for Rathbone's Corsets. How he had ended up there, he wasn't entirely sure, although he had worked in sales ever since leaving Bolton tech with an HNC in Joinery and Coffin-making. His first sales job was for the chain of undertakers he was apprenticed to, but his heart wasn't really in it. He was successful as a salesman, but the urge to sell a more lively, more interesting product was always present.

He'd considered selling marine diesel engines, rat traps, trusses, surgical appliances and patent medicines. Before Rathbone's, his last job was selling specialist paints to industry, but still he yearned for excitement and the exotic. It was this yearning for a more colourful, stimulating... fulfilling career that led him to apply for the job of Marketing Manager at Rathbone's Corsets.

Ted had, since his teens, been fascinated by large mature ladies. Their voluptuousness was captivating. Over the years, he had amassed a great deal of printed material on large ladies. He would retrieve mother's discarded – and now outdated – mail order catalogues, cutting out and keeping the pages from the corsetry and ladies underwear sections. These were filed away in an ever-increasing collection of loose-leaf binders stored between steam railway books.

After finishing the apprenticeship, Ted had attended night school, studying marketing, which he found both interesting and engaging. The most useful concept he came away with, after a successful graduation, was "niche marketing."

Niche marketing was the theme of his pitch during the job interview at Rathbone's Corsets. He pointed out to the board that, although the market for their products was large (most ladies being size sixteen and above), it was still a niche market. The scattergun broadcast advertising they used wasn't specifically targeting this customer base. He got the job.

For the first week or so, he familiarised himself with the product range. For Ted, it was bliss. The ladies who modelled were large, often mature, and uninhibited. He had not seen so many – to him – attractive ladies in their underwear together at one time. As a result, Ted was aroused much of the time to the amusement of the ladies concerned.

After the third week, he called the design team to the sales office, together with Alice, Rathbone's most popular model. Alice was of medium height, in her late forties and attractive, with short grey straight hair, a generous bosom and ample bottom.

Alice was modelling one of their faster-moving lines: a formidable white corset that bound her in an iron-like grip. It had straps buckles and laces. With the corset, she wore stockings, white knickers, shoes and nothing else.

Ted managed to keep himself under control; the spectacle of these ladies in a state of undress was still new to him. He stood up carefully and approached Alice, then turned to the design team, thankful for his loosely cut trousers.

"For the purpose of this exercise, imagine Alice and I are up to a bit of hanky-panky. We are getting rather passionate and I try to access her naughty bits. Would I need bolt croppers or a hacksaw?

"I want you to go away and design me a garment that celebrates large bottoms and big busts, makes large ladies even more attractive to the men that desire them but, most importantly, accessible. Is that clear?"

The three women and one man that made up the design team nodded their assent but one of the older ladies seemed far from happy. Ted looked her in the eye.

"Is there a problem Judith?"

"It all seems a little indecent to me. I always believed ladies should be modest and decently dressed."

"Look on it as a challenge. We are looking to celebrate abundant femininity, not suppress it."

The team left the office. After putting on her dressing gown, so did Alice. Even with the protection of her formidable corset, she was unsure of Ted.

When Ted had first set eyes on Agnes, it was love at first sight. At the time, Ted was selling paint. Whilst walking through the workshop of Ganderho forge, on his way to the buyer's office, he stopped to watch – mesmerised – the final forging of a small ship's anchor.

The anchor was lifted from the fire by a crane, its metal a glowing, whitish yellow. It was lowered onto a huge anvil, still supported by the crane's chain as one man held it in place. An old man – the master smith – picked up a hammer, first tapping the side of the anvil then striking the anchor handling a three-pound hammer as anyone else would a teaspoon.

As he lifted his hammer from the anchor, first one then the other striker hit the same spot full force with a fourteen-pound sledgehammer. The smith continued to hit the anchor and the strikers would follow each time with blows to the same spot, sparks flying every time a hammer landed.

After some minutes, the smith struck the side of the anvil again and the hammering ceased. The anchor cooled slowly, turning first cherry then dark red, before blackening.

Ted was amazed to see one of the strikers was a woman. He looked into her bright eyes and was smitten.

Agnes was tall for a woman, large and muscular. Her brown hair, bound in a blue turban, escaped from it in places. Her eyes twinkled from a face darkened by smoke.

He'd waited for her to clock out at the factory gate that evening, a bunch of roses in his hands. He gave her the roses and asked her for a date. Surprised – both by the roses and the request – she agreed.

They were soon meeting regularly, becoming inseparable on their free evenings.

A few weeks after the design team meeting, Alice reappeared before Ted and the team. She took off her dressing gown, revealing the newly designed blue corset, accompanied only by her stockings, knickers and shoes.

Ted immediately sat down and crossed his legs, his face flushed.

Judith turned to him and said archly, "I think we have the balance right don't you Mr. Crouch? It is a quite stimulating design isn't it? Turn round Alice, let him see the view from behind." She deftly brushed Alice's bottom. "I think it has accentuated Alice's curvature beautifully don't you, Mr Crouch? Liberated, yet controlled, but above all accessible."

She went on to point out the salient features of the garment: the suspenders, the stiffening, the materials used, and how comfort, practicality, wearability, washabiliy – as well as accessibility – had all been considered.

Ted went to speak, croaked, cleared his throat and tried again.

"That is brilliant, Judith – and all of you. That is exactly what I was looking for; you have excelled yourselves."

The new corset was given the name the Blue Angel, inspired by the Marlene Dietrich film. It was agreed that Alice should wear the corset for a few days to assess how practical and comfortable it was for everyday use, and she was given two to try.

The following Monday the design and sales teams met again to discuss how the garment had stood up to daily use. Alice removed her dressing gown and stood before them dressed as before. She had a sparkle in her eyes that Ted hadn't noticed earlier.

"How did it go Alice?" he asked.

"Very well, thank you," replied Alice

"Was it comfortable?"

"Yes – very much so. After about ten minutes I wasn't conscious of it at all. I forgot I was wearing a corset. My husband loved it."

"Did he?"

"When he arrived home from work, I was in the kitchen.

"The dress I was wearing fitted differently – my bottom and bust were more prominent. He noticed immediately and made me take my dress and slip off, right there in the kitchen. I just managed to get to the bedroom before him; I haven't seen him so excited for years."

"And accessibility?"

"Brilliant. The small zip between the cups is a masterstroke."

"The Free-float Device?" Interjected Judith.

Ted gave her a quizzical glance.

"It allows each breast to move separately but be adequately supported. When worn under a dress or blouse it gives the impression, to a degree, that the lady is bra-less. It also allows easier access."

"Was this your idea, Judith?" asked Ted

Judith bashfully admitted she was responsible.

"Well done, Judith. This is a masterstroke. There will be a bonus for you and the team."

Ted wanted Agnes to model the corset for the promotional photographs, with the other models standing round in a tableau, similarly dressed. Agnes would be seated, wearing the corset, matching blue knickers, black stockings, long black gloves, a top hat, and black high-heeled shoes.

Agnes wasn't keen on modelling. Though confident in her work and at ease with herself, she didn't want to be photographed in her underwear. Ted asked Alice and the other ladies if they would try to persuade her.

The following Saturday, Agnes arrived with Ted at the offices of Rathbone's corset factory, the venue for the photo-shoot.

Ted had left the decision to Agnes. She would talk to the others and, if confident, she would model the corset for the photos. If not, Alice or another model would take her place.

An office had been set aside as a changing room and a makeup artist was on hand, as were several bottles of wine and large glasses.

The product launch was a huge success; Agnes shone in her first modelling assignment. A successful advertising campaign followed, bringing a tumultuous wave of orders.

Success brought Agnes other modelling offers. The magazines "Large Lass" and "Big Girl" soon beat a path to her door. Agnes left the forge and went to London to pursue her modelling career, leaving Ted behind, heartbroken.

Ted and Tracy parted on Sunday without arranging to meet again. On Monday evening, Ted came home from a quiet day at work, sad to be returning to an empty flat. He unlocked the front door

On the hall table was a black top hat and a pair of long black gloves. His heart raced.

Agnes's voice came from the bedroom.

"What's a girl got to do to get serviced round here? I've made a start by taking some of my clothes off – get a move on."

Ted rushed to the bedroom, undressing as best he could en route.

~~~

POETIC FENLAND

Inspired by our surroundings

...

The Fens

Caroline Cowan

Fen villages, church spires, people, pubs and farms,
Landscapes, huge skies, a feeling of open space.
Ploughed field, wet earth,
   brown and grey, sticky clay,

Leafless trees, thick hedges, patchwork of colours.
Tractor trails, deep furrows, crops all planted.
Daffodils sway, yellow carpet, spring time!
Turned soil, hungry birds,
   insects, wriggly brown worms.

Dykes dug, foreign prisoners, watery grave, R.I.P.
Pumping-house, derelict buildings, all forgotten.
Marshy areas, reed beds, mating birds, butterflies.
Rare plants, buzzing bees, flashes of bright colours.

Swans nesting, cob and pen, keeping eggs warm.
Hovering mist, eerie silence, where's the sun?
Superstitions, witches, will o' the wisp.
Dog barking, kettle whistling, home sweet home.

~~~

A Typical Fen Night

Wendy Fletcher

We live in a house
Right out in the Fens.
You know where I mean,
Just as the world ends.

The front room is up,
The kitchen is down.
Outside is the risk
That you'll likely drown.

As the house floats free
On our reed-bed raft,
Carried by the water
On its endless path
We lift and fall,
Swirling as we goes.
Are we risin' or fallin'?
Nobody knows.

We old Fen folk
Just 'old the table tight
And talk of times gone
When things never were right.

We tell the tales of
Deluge and disaster,
Of animals lost
And fields awash
And worse to come after.

Shifting the gault,
Topping the banks,
The dykes overflow.
The moon is shining
On acres of water
with nowhere to go

Crowland's danger bell
Peals through the night.
A warning too late
To save the ghosts
Who screech and cry,
'Those blasted weathermen never git it right.'

But we won't worry.
We know the sluice at Denver
Will catch our fall,
Before we finish up
No-where at all.

~~~

Living in Fenland

Val Chapman

"Why on earth did you move out here?"
Said my family, seeking clarification.
To be fair, it's a question I've asked myself
On more than one occasion.

Maybe it's the acres of sky,
Or the fields that stretch out for miles.
Could it be the beautiful sunsets?
Some of the best in the British Isles.

Sunrises that look like the sky is on fire?
Or the sight of a heron in flight?
A glimpse of a deer, a pheasant, a hare,
Or the bats and the badgers at night?

There are plenty of folks who like cities,
I'm sure they too have their charm.
But for me, all the wide open spaces,
Leave me peaceful, and rested, and calm.

Yes, I'm pleased to be living in Fenland.
The locals are fine, by and large.

Even those 'passing through' as I walk by the Nene
Give a cheery 'hello' from their barge.

I'm done with the crowded and smoky;
I've left all of that behind.
It's the flat, unassuming Fen landscape
That, for now, brings me peace of mind.

So really, why *am* I here?
The answer's the easiest yet,
It's just to avoid the struggle up hills,
Which get steeper, the older I get.

~~~

Alien Landscape

Cathy Cade

My window frames an unfamiliar picture
when I rise.
Why am I here?
Behind the glass, an alien landscape lies.
White mist rising like dry ice
is merging with grey skies.

Last week I woke to sparrow-song
as streetlights bowed to dawn.
Here, screeching scavengers squabble
over something small and torn.
A flat world full of emptiness,
where courage fails, stillborn.

Mist rising now, a ghost-white disc
peers through the weakening shroud.
The distant skeletons of trees
stand out against pale cloud,
And fields are stubble-beige
– or ordure brown where newly ploughed.

Beneath the window, suddenly
a glimpse of furry grey,
Where something hops out of the dyke
and pauses on its way,
Its long ears quivering, nostrils twitching,
taking in the day.

Overhead, the veil dissolves;
the sun is burning through.
Behind the haze, the sky's an endless dome
of milky blue.
Sunbeams brush my window's frame
and paint the scene anew.

Beneath my window, leaf buds on the tree
are dewdrop-pearled.
While in the field across the drove,
green blades show, tightly curled.
A new life beckons
in a yet-to-be-discovered world.

~~~

Voices of Wicken

Wendy Fletcher

The wind whispering
through the reed beds
tells the tale of those
who trod this land,
carving their course,
sculpting the scene,
in sun and shadow.
alone with the fen.

Tired and weary,
worn by weather,
young bodies bowed
but resolute.
They strove to live,
from this unforgiving
land, a life bound
only by the fen.

These are the men
whose breath
is the mist.

These are the men
whose ghosts
rustle the reeds.

~~~

The Fens (very briefly)

Philip Cumberland

For the last ten thousand years, or thereabouts, the story of the fens has been about mankind's struggle with the environment. Many were willing to live with the landscape nature had given them – sources of food by way of fish and wildfowl, building materials of oak willow and reed, fuel from peat or wood. The abundance of eels gave Ely its name.

Others saw the inundation, the waters, as a barrier to the cultivation of rich soil and easy movement through the land. Since at least Roman times, efforts had been made to reclaim land from the waters, but it wasn't until the seventeenth century that serious progress was made.

The name forever linked to the assault on the wetlands is that of Cornelius Vermuyden. A Dutchman, commissioned originally in 1629 by the Crown to drain Hatfield chase situated in Lincolnshire's Isle of Axholme, Vermuyden went on to direct the draining of the East Anglian Fens during the 1650s. Once drained, the now arable land was enclosed and claimed by those adventurers who had financed the drainage works.

The original fen-dwellers, who lived off the undrained fens by wildfowling, fishing, reed harvesting and osier gathering, were often hostile to these changes. Rioting occurred and, in some places, dykes were filled in as quickly as they were being dug. Oliver Cromwell made one of his earliest speeches in Parliament supporting constituents who opposed fen drainage at Holme. In later years, he changed his position to support drainage.

Before the fens were extensively drained, they were used as a means of water-borne communication and for the transportation of goods. In this way, much of the stone used to construct local churches and abbeys was moved from Barnack, where it was quarried. At Sawtry, a canal was dug to the main body of water, Whittlesey Mere, to allow stone to be brought to the construction site of the abbey. Many parishes to the west of Whittlesey Mere were narrow, with access to the water to allow trade.

The waters were also used for recreation. King Cnute used Ugg Mere for sport, and two of his sons are believed to have drowned in the Mere. Their bodies are buried under the floor of the dining room in Bodsey House.

Early maps show Fen towns, villages and hamlets as islands surrounded by waters. Travel between them during the winter months and wet periods would be impossible in most cases without boats or stilts.

As rivers, drains and dykes were dug, the drying land tended to sink. The light peat soil was easily blown away by the wind, eroding and lowering soil levels further. Before long, many of the main waterways were above the level of the surrounding land, necessitating the need for pumping.

Early pumps were wind powered, similar in appearance to windmills. Energy captured by the sails was converted by gearing to drive scoop wheels – a reverse version of a water wheel – and lift the water from low-level drainage dykes, discharging it into higher channels which fed into drains or rivers

Dependent, as they were, on the vagaries of the winds, this method was of limited use. Steam power made for a more reliable means of drainage. The early steam engines were used to drive scoop wheels in much the same way as wind power, although the greater power allowed larger scoop wheels to be employed. Eventually, more efficient turbine pumps were introduced as they became available.

Diesel powered pumps gradually replaced most of the steam pumping engines once they were available as a reliable alternative. They offered greater power and fuel efficiency, although a few steam powered pumping stations survived.

The steam-powered Streatham Old Engine was last used in 1947. This is a large beam engine driving a scoop wheel. As, by then, its boilers were not considered safe, steam was provided by a traction engine. Streatham Old Engine is now a museum: well worth a visit. There is another drainage museum at Prick Willow, which houses a collection of diesel powered drainage pumps.

Most diesel powered pumping stations were, in turn, replaced by electrically-driven pumps; the largest pumping station is at St Germans. Eighty smaller pumping stations feed water into the system that supplies St Germans. The six pumps at St Germans can each shift a volume of water equivalent to that of a double-decker bus, every second. If all six pumps are running, they can pump a volume of water equivalent to five Olympic-size swimming pools every two minutes. These electrically driven pumps are supplied with mains power supplemented or replaced, as necessary, by on-site diesel generators.

Large-scale Ordnance Survey maps show the complexity and size of the fen drainage system. The maps show extensive grids of blue lines, denoting the ditches, dykes and rivers needed to keep the land dry.

Old maps show a landscape far different from today; the Fens must have been a fascinating place back then. Places where villages exist now were once areas of mere, with land surfaces covered mostly in water and roads scarce or non-existent.

The antiquity of fen settlements can often be gauged by the age of churches or chapels situated within them. The oldest settlements – Whittlesey, Ramsey, March, Chatteris – have medieval or earlier churches, whilst Ramsey Mereside, for instance, has a Victorian chapel. The church at Ramsey St Mary's, although of older appearance, was built in 1859.

There is no sign of Ramsey Mereside, Ramsey Forty-Foot, Ramsey Heights or Ramsey St Mary's on an 1848 map of Huntingdonshire. This is unsurprising since many fens and meres were still open water. Ramsey Mereside's ground height is 0.7m below sea level.

The Fens have produced some remarkable people of independent thought – often very influential. Probably the most famous son of Huntingdon and the Fens was Oliver Cromwell, the country's first republican head of state – his son Richard being, so far, the only other.

Thomas Clarkson was a leading anti-slavery campaigner, born in Wisbech. He did much of the work to bring about the abolition of slavery achieved by the Wilberforce Act.

Whittlesey gave the world Sir Harry Smith, a famous nineteenth century soldier and statesman. One of my great, great, uncles was given the names Harry Smith as forenames, although at that time the family was living in Spaldwick.

The undrained fens were not only a home for wildfowl, fish and eels but also for a variety of insects, including the mosquito.

Living in pools of stagnant water, these spread a form of Malaria known as the Ague or Fen Ague. Famous sufferers of the Ague were Samuel Pepys and Oliver Cromwell – in Cromwell's case a recurring bout of the disease proved fatal.

Eventually fen drainage reduced open pools of stagnant water where the mosquitoes bred, and the Ague disappeared. It is hoped that the re-establishment of large wetlands, such as the Great Fen Project, will not encourage the return of mosquitoes and with them the Ague.

Sir Harry Godwin is quoted as saying, "Any fool can appreciate mountain scenery, but it takes a man of discernment to appreciate the Fens."

Helen R Kirk, on her blog, attributes this quote to a resident of the Cambridgeshire Fens speaking to the famous botanist.

I do not claim to have great discernment but I do appreciate our Fen landscape with its spectacular sunsets and skies. I hope others do too.

~~~

City Boy

Wendy Fletcher

I watch you swinging gently,
A piece of old wood for a seat,
Suspended on rope from a branch
Of the old gnarled apple tree

You were not born in time to see
My grandmother planting that pip,
You did not know her weathered face,
Nor hear the step of slippered feet,

And I wonder, Grandson, what
she would have made of you.
With jeans bought 'ready torn',
Base-ball cap from a London shop.

I wonder what she would make
Of your walk, your talk, City Boy.
I-Pods, are they like pea-pods?
Blackberries for tunes, not for tea?

She could not understand your world
Nor recognise your words,
Your urban accent strange to these parts,
Not nurtured in the Fens,

Would be the foreign tongue
of a city never seen.
But I laugh now as you call to me,
'Grandma, can we make some jam?'

All's not lost, the world moves on,
But crossing five generations
I see a shadowy figure
Smile, to greet you home, City Boy.

~~~

Ode to the Fens

Jan Cunningham

I do not like thee Mistress Fen.
You promised much, but then
You caught me unawares,

With your damp mists and boggyness,
Your brooding skies and sogginess,
Your blustery showers of black fen soot,
Your dykes and drains of forty foot.
I look for trees and scarce see any.
Reeds and rushes there are many;
Miles and miles of flattened land
With ne'er a tor nor hill on hand.
No bushes, shrubs or flowering hedgerows,
Just mile upon mile of deep dark furrows

I do not like thee Mistress Fen.

~~~

STARTING IN THE MIDDLE

Open a book and pick a prompt.

(We've since taken out the original prompts
for copyright reasons)

.

Tiddly Pom

Cathy Cade

'The Transmundane Worlds Investigation Team has been asked to look into reports of unusual activity near East Grinstead.'

The director's self-important air suggested another time-wasting digression for her team. The professer hid her irritation.

'What kind of unusual activity?'

'Unexpected sightings, untypical owl activity, unauthorised animals...'

'Unauthorised?'

'Not sheep or cows – which is all that are registered to graze the common at present.'

'So we're talking about the common?'

'More specifically, Ashdown Forest.'

'Ah.' The professor knew the area. It was popular with tourists, some of whom had strange ideas about holiday snaps.

Director Ellis Jobson continued. 'Disgusted-of-Tunbridge-Wells has been writing to the papers again, blaming the local council for "a feeling" he's experienced when walking his dog in the woods.'

'Not old Disgusted? He must, surely, be dead by now?'

'They think it might be a relative.' The director waved a hand, dismissing the digression.

'The thing is... the readings *are* registering some kind of radiation. Electromagnetic fields have been irregular.'

'Like the alien sightings in Wales, you mean?'

She knew the director was having a battle to retain funding for the department, but... 'Didn't they turn out to be sheep?'

'That's what the press were told – we don't want to incite panic, after all. But a number of temperance chapel-goers were convinced they'd heard voices from those sheep.'

The professor believed their research grant could be better spent elsewhere, but she wisely kept this opinion to herself, allowing Director Jobson to continue.

'Then there were those sightings near Glastonbury and the girl who claimed she'd been taken up into a spaceship.'

'Yes, well...'

'Her friends backed her up,' the director reminded her. 'We are obliged to investigate these reports, whatever you may think of their credibility.'

The professor suspected the whole Glastonbury group had been on something left over from the Festival, but the director persisted.

'Nobody's ever explained that battle on Wimbledon Common, between the Wombles and the Teletubbies.

We have substantial film footage sent in from spectators' mobile phones.'

The professor had often wondered why there were so many spectators on Wimbledon Common after midnight on the first of April... but she was as keen as the director to hang on to her job.

'I'll get a group together to investigate,' she said.

The meter reading was off the scale, but they were unable to identify the nature of the radiation.

'It feels... sort of prickly,' said a research student.

'Fresh,' said her boyfriend. 'New – like the air after a storm.'

The professor was directing the taking of soil samples when another researcher came striding out of the woods.

'It's snowing on the other side of those trees,' he said. 'Why isn't it snowing here?'

They followed him into the woods.

An owl watched them from a low branch of a tree bordering the area known locally as Five Hundred Acre Wood.

'Who-you?' it said

Just past the first trees, two of the research group were having a snowball fight.

Others marched arm-in-arm around the clearing singing.

'The more it snows,
'Tiddly Pom,
'The more it snows,
'Tiddly Pom,
'The more it goes...
'Tiddly Pom
'...on snowing.'

The students accompanying the professor joined in.
'And nobody knows
'Tiddly Pom
'How cold my toes
'Tiddly Pom...'

The professor resisted the impulse to join them; she had noticed a trail of footprints.

The shapeless dents in the snow alternated at regular intervals. Beside them, tiny pinpricks of footprints skipped a space every few steps. They led her into a clearing, where a large stuffed teddy bear sat on a fallen tree trunk beside a small toy pig.

She stopped, unable to believe her eyes. An owl flew down to perch on the shoulder of the bear.

'Goo-ood evening, Professor,' said the owl.

Now, she didn't believe her ears.

'Do-hoo sit down.' The owl's wing indicated an unoccupied section of tree trunk.

'Yes, p-please join us,' said the pig.

'I suppose you haven't brought any honey?' asked the bear.

The professor found her voice. 'I don't believe–'

'Yoo-hoo don't believe we've met,' interrupted the owl. 'But we have, yoooo know. Many years ago.'

'I'm Winnie-the-Pooh,' said the bear, 'and this is my best friend, Piglet. That is Wol... and you are Jane Slightly.'

'How do you know?'

'From the stories – although your ancestor came from a different one.'

'But I don't believe–' the animals gasped '–those stories were real.'

Tension drained from the group.

'No,' said Wol. 'Nobody does any more.'

He drew himself up to his full height.

'Ahem. You see children know such a lot now, they soon stop believing in fairies, and every time a child says, "I don't believe in fairies," there is a fairy somewhere that falls down dead.'

Jane felt as if her head was filled with stuffing, like the toys.

'I'm sure I've heard that before.'

'Possibly from your great-grandfather,' said Wol. 'I'm quoting from *Peter Pan and Wendy*.' He shook his feathers. 'The trouble is, young people have access to more information now, and they believe most of it.'

'Especially if it's on F-facebook,' said Piglet.

'They were better off believing in fairies,' said Pooh.

'It's called the Tinkerbell Effect,' said Wol. 'There's a Reverse Tinkerbell Effect too – thinking that if enough people believe something it becomes true.'

'I'm sorry,' said Professor Jane. 'You've lost me.'

Wol continued anyway. 'Imagine all that un-anchored belief woo-ooshing around the world, attaching itself to the most unlikely fantasies.'

'We do what we can to soak some of it up,' said Pooh. 'It's the way we were written.'

'And at least *we're* harmless,' said Piglet.

'Especially Pooh,' added the owl.

But the professor still didn't understand.

'Well, have you ever heard someone say, "I don't believe in Winnie-the-Pooh"?' asked Piglet.

'Or, "I don't believe in Wallace and Grommit"?' said Wol, 'or Shaun the Sheep?'

'Or the Wombles?' offered Pooh.

'You mean, if I were to say–'

'Don't say it!' Three voices chorused in unison.

Just then, a conga line of research scholars snaked through the trees.

'...Tiddly Pom,

'How cold my toes

'Tiddly Pom,

'How cold my toes

'Tiddly Pom,

'Are GRO...wi...ng...'

One by one, they stopped as they saw the toys. The researchers huddled together uncertainly.

'Professor?'

'Um, yes... Meet Winnie-the-Pooh, Piglet and Wol.

'Those are brilliant costumes,' said one researcher.

Wol sighed. 'We ought to-oo go now,' he said. 'It was nice meeting yoo-hoo, Jane.'

He flew up as the bear stood and held out a hand for the piglet. They shuffled into the trees.

'That's not a costume,' said another research student. 'Piglet's too small, and people don't fly. That really is them.'

'Don't be silly,' sneered a third. 'You may believe in talking Pooh-bears, owls and piglets, but I don't.'

A gentle thump could be heard, as of something hitting the ground. The receding figures were gone.

The research group trailed back through the woods. Snow was melting and the air smelled... ordinary. When they reached the equipment they had brought with them, it registered no radiation at all.

Each of them struggled to recall the brief elation they had felt. The mood was subdued; little was said. Only the professor was heard to mutter, 'I don't believe in Ellis Jobson... I don't believe in Ellis Jobson.'

~~

Beachhampton Towers

Caroline Cowan

"You went for dinner at Beachhampton Towers, didn't you?" I asked.

"How did you find out, Caroline?" she snapped back at me.

Julia and I were twins with extra powers. We each felt the other's pain, and both experienced Extra Sensory Perception (ESP) We were very close for the first sixteen years, but then things changed between us. Julia started pulling away from me and going out with her own set of friends. I couldn't understand the reason for this, as we had always shared our secrets and friends.

Julia had completed an accounts course at college and was now working in the nearby town of Broxborough, whilst I had gone on to do a nursing degree and was now working in the hospital near Broxborough. I accepted Julia's separation and got on with my life. I knew it wasn't any good questioning her about the issue; she had always had a short fuse. I, the younger by minutes, was the easy-going one.

Our parents had moved away to live in Spain and left us to look after the house. We had always been trustworthy and never caused them much grief whilst growing up. They had invited us to join them abroad, but we hadn't wanted to give up our jobs to start again, so they left us to look after everything, although they often phoned with updates on how they were doing.

For our twenty-first birthday Julia had, for once, asked if I would like to join her on a night out to the village of Witchington, which was on the coast a couple miles away from where we lived in Hellington.

"I would love to Julia. It will be like old times."

She gave me an odd look and then nodded agreement. "There's a lovely little pub which serves delicious food. We can catch up, and I'll introduce you to some of my friends. Seven o'clock alright for you?"

"I'll be ready and waiting, Julia."

When seven o'clock came and we set off to the pub, I chatted casually but Julia, although friendly, still kept her distance.

The pub was an oldie-worldie one with horse-brasses hanging round the bar and pictures of Witchington from past to present.

Julia introduced me to some of the people she hung around with and, after chatting for some time, we ate a delicious meal and drank a few glasses of wine – it was celebration time, after all. This was turning out to be an enjoyable evening, and I thought how friendly everyone was. It was good to see a little of the old Julia re--surfacing.

"Now for your next surprise." said Julia. "You are going to have a tour round Beachhampton Towers. I know you have always been fascinated by old houses."

I was shocked and thrilled at the same time.

"I always thought it was out of bounds to the locals." It was rumoured to have guard dogs patrolling the grounds, though none had ever been seen. "How did you manage to arrange that, Sis?"

"Oh, I have my contacts," Julia answered nonchalantly.

I thought we would be on our own, but no – Julia's friends were coming as well. I did think this a little odd but accepted that they wanted to share in Julia's birthday too. They were her friends, after all – though it would have been nice for just us two to sit and chat.

Beachhampton Towers was within walking distance, and I hoped the short walk would clear my head, which was fuzzy after the wine.

It was a dark and imposing building: a mediaeval mansion.

"Wow," I exclaimed as it came into view. "Creepy, isn't it?"

I had read every piece of literature I could find on this curious house. It had, supposedly, been associated with a coven of witches in its distant past. Julia had always been interested in the occult, but I had stayed clear of all that; I didn't want to get involved. The house had caverns beneath. A tunnel was supposed to lead to the pub and another to the beach. The sea was close and must fill the tunnels at high tide. It was around the time of the month when the moon was full.

The owner of the house was a Sir Simon Humphrey who, Julia said, would show me around the premises. I felt honoured. One thing I now noticed was that everyone was wearing a medallion. All bore the same signs, which reminded me of something from the past... but my head was too woozy to think straight. Was it the Freemasons or something else?

We were taken along winding passages into the caverns; I felt sure I would never find my way out unaided. Giggling to myself, I thought I should have left a trail of breadcrumbs to help me then realised I was still a little tipsy.

The caverns were huge. They were dark with a strange odour and an atmosphere which seemed to press down on me. An eerie glow emanated from the candles that burned in large candlesticks round the walls.

My head span... and then I fainted.

I woke up, unsure how long I had been out. Disorientated, I couldn't move. I struggled but was unable to free myself.

I was tied to a cold slab in the middle of the cavern. Strange chanting came from a group of cloaked, hooded figures circling the cavern. Standing over me, was a woman.

The chanting grew louder until the woman above me raised a knife. The steel glinted in the candlelight. I could not move or speak. Had they drugged me or chanted some spell over me?

My head was clearing, and I was beginning to think more clearly. Panic hadn't set in; for some reason, I remained calm. Then I recognised the woman standing over me.

Julia!

My sister was a witch, and not just a witch but a High Priestess.

Why? What had I done to deserve this?

I hadn't thought witches existed any more but here they were in the caverns of Beachhampton Towers, and I was their next victim. I wondered how many had been sacrificed before me. Would my heart be cut out and eaten? my blood drunk to purify them, by orders of... I didn't even want to think of who had ordered this. I couldn't even say his name! The chanting was reaching its peak as they faced an altar on the cavern wall. I was glad I couldn't see what they were looking at. I knew it was evil.

I began to plead with Julia, using our ESP and hoping I could get through to her.

"How can you do this to me? We are twins. We grew up together. We have helped each other through thick and thin. We shared each other's aches and pains We love each other."

"You are to be sacrificed, to please our Master."

Her voice sounded different. The knife slowly raised above her head and the chanting continued, but I had to keep trying to get through to her.

"Julia, remember we are more than family; we are truly connected from birth."

I visualised some of the happy times we had spent together from childhood and thought I saw something change in her eyes. I carried on with my reminiscing, willing her to listen, and felt sure the old Julia was emerging from somewhere deep inside.

Suddenly the knife came down. I closed my eyes tight... then opened them slowly, realising I was still alive and my bonds were loose.

"Quick, Caroline, run for the door while you can."

"Come with me Julia," I pleaded. "Start afresh."

"No, it's too late for me."

The door opened of its own accord, and I ran through without looking back. I realised then what powers she must have attained over the years.

The door slammed shut behind me, and I ran as fast as I could, trying to remember the way out. Somehow, I found myself in the fresh air and kept going until well out of the village.

Nobody seemed to be following me.

It took about an hour – half running, half walking – to get home. Even there, I didn't feel safe.

It was then I remembered about the high tide and realised the caverns were probably flooded by now. I wondered if they were trapped there, or if they had powers to materialise somewhere else. Then I felt silly at the thought but, somewhere at the back of my mind, I didn't feel that Julia was dead.

My parents were at the airport to meet me in sunny Spain. Pleased to see me, they welcomed me with open arms. I felt safer just being with them.

I made an excuse for my sudden arrival, omitting the story of the witches coven and Julia being the High Priestess. I told them she spent a lot of time in Witchington and not at home, and they accepted this without questioning me further – almost like strangers instead of our parents. Something wasn't quite right. I buried my thoughts and just enjoyed being with them.

So I started a new life in Spain, nursing in the large hospital there. The staff were pleased to have an English nurse and would utilise me as a translator as well as a nurse.

My Spanish was improving, and in a few months I would have enough money for a small apartment of my own. I had settled in and was enjoying life.

One evening, as my parents went out I wished them a happy evening, saying I would see them later. Life seemed good for us all.

It was then I noticed the medallions – like the ones from the coven – on chains around their necks.

They smiled at me as they shut the door.

~~~

A Dinner to Die For

Val Chapman

"You went for dinner at Barton House, didn't you?"

Sue put down her knife and looked across the table to her friend.

"Oh God, yes. It was amazing – a brilliant night. It was hilarious until Paul Hetherington died."

Ruth almost choked on her salmon and asparagus quiche.

"Bloody hell, Sue, I had no idea. What on earth happened?"

"Well, yeah, it was a bit of a surprise, I must say.

"We'd all gone out from work to celebrate finally getting to the end of the project, and everyone was up for having a good time. The organiser met us in the entrance hall, gave us some champagne and took us through to the room where all the tables had been set out. Beautifully decorated – had a very 'twenties' look, I thought.

"Anyway, there were quite a few of us, as some of the contractors had been invited too. Like I said, we were enjoying ourselves and mingled a bit before we sat down for the first course – caramelised onion and goat's cheese tart, if you're interested. It was gorgeous.

"I'd been chatting with June and Rob, and the main course was being served when we noticed a bit of a commotion at one of the other tables. Some bloke had just collapsed on the floor. People were staring, unsure what was going on, and some of the staff were running about.

"Then it all went quiet, and someone – I think it was Roger – said that he was dead. Paul Hetherington I mean, not Roger."

Ruth was fascinated

"Ooh, it gives me the shivers just thinking about it." She didn't let that stop her though. "So what happened then? Did you know him?"

"Well, I knew *of* him but hadn't had many dealings with him. There were a few giggles, as if people couldn't believe it, and then everyone started asking questions, because someone said he'd been murdered and we weren't allowed to leave.

"Andrea works in HR, and she said she thought he'd been having an affair with either Brian, or Bryony, she wasn't sure which. Then someone – I think it might have been Julian – said they'd heard some important computer details had been stolen and suspected that this Paul Hetherington person might have been involved. Honestly, I think he's been watching too many James Bond movies.

"You wouldn't believe some of the theories about why this bloke might have been killed.

"It was interesting, actually, watching the way people behaved. There were definitely some shifty-looking faces around. But, on the whole, everyone seemed really clued up about what to do.

"So, we all listened, and talked, and tried to ask the right questions, and worked out that he'd been embezzling money from the owner of Barton House for years, and the fella who owns it had managed to poison his dinner.

"Honestly, Ruth, these 'Murder Mystery' nights are brilliant!"

~~~

The Manor

Wendy Fletcher

'You went to dinner at The Manor, didn't you?'

Louise was trying to focus on the voice but it hovered somewhere just above her bed, coming closer and swinging away again as the room revolved. A male voice.

Who was this?

Was it the police?

Her head swam as she squinted to see if there were uniforms in the room.

Had she been attacked? She certainly felt sick enough to make it a possibility.

Had she been drugged?

Surely not...

John Browning-Porter had been the perfect host. She remembered arriving, how he took her coat. She had shivered at the feel of his warm fingers on her neck as he helped her out of it.

Snippets of conversation fluttered around her head. Why wasn't Gordon here by her side?

They'd had a bit of a quarrel when she insisted on going to the dinner on her own after Gordon had rung to say he would be home too late to accompany her.

Well, not actually on her own, just without him. There were other guests, of course. She recalled a chorus of undulating voices and a waft of expensive perfume.

Had she stayed too late? She couldn't pull together a picture of herself leaving.

Oh, surely she hadn't stayed... an image of the handsome John Browning-Porter's smile shimmied across her line of vision. She felt again the fleeting brush of fingers on her neck.

Could she really have been seduced into staying too long, perhaps after everyone else had gone home?

Oh no, she pleaded, could she have put herself in such a position?

Might the gentle John Browning-Porter have turned on her if she later resisted his attention?

Or could Gordon have turned up late and found her in some compromising position?

Was there a confrontation? Had she stepped between the two men and taken the first testosterone-fuelled blow?

Never in her life had she had two men fighting over her; the idea was ludicrous.

But it would explain how she felt: make sense of the fact that her skull was bursting, her eyes wouldn't focus, and her stomach churned, even before these images made her retch. She found it difficult focussing on such possibilities to investigate their likelihood.

The sinking emptiness shifted from her stomach to her heart.

Had she really been unfaithful to Gordon? Had he arrived too late to pull her back from the brink of destroying everything they had built over the last four years? Had she been stupid enough to let go of all that she valued, just because Gordon was late home from work and John Browning-Porter had incredibly soft hands?

Despite her inability to move a muscle, she felt a single tear form in her left eye and fall.

'Oh, look.' The voice was soft and female.

'That's a good sign.' It was the male voice again.

'We need to find out what they all ate, so that we can establish the source of this outbreak.'

~~~

Dinner at Hyams House

Cathy Cade

It had been raining for most of his journey home, but Jane's car was still on the drive when he pulled in behind it. She would regret not putting it away when she got in to find a puddle in the footwell. Something would have be done about that leak when it went in for servicing next week.

He retrieved his weekend case from the boot and noticed the garage door wasn't properly shut – so much for security! He pushed the door up to check inside but, luckily, the rain hadn't flooded the garage floor yet. It usually did it when the door was open.

He saw she'd left the door into the house unlatched too – his wife would forget her head if it wasn't screwed on.

He pulled the door down and tested that the latch had caught properly.

Jane wasn't in the kitchen. He filled the kettle and turned it on. As he took his favourite mug from the cupboard, and one for Jane, he heard her go into the bathroom. She didn't linger there; the kettle was boiling as she came downstairs. He called to her.

'Cup of tea?'

She entered the kitchen in her bathroobe. 'Yes please. You're back early.'

'I left after breakfast. I didn't see much point hanging around for the valedictory session – it'll just be the Chairman telling us what a successful conference it's been. You left the garage door open. The door through to the hall wasn't locked either. You must be more careful about locking up when I'm not here.'

'You should have let me know you'd be back, Peter. I'd have had something ready.'

'You weren't in when I rang last night, and your mobile was turned off.'

'The battery ran out.'

'You went to dinner at Hyams House, didn't you?'

Jane looked at him blankly. She didn't seem the full shilling this morning, as if she'd slept badly.

'Er – Yes.' She seemed surprised at his deductive powers. He felt rather pleased with them himself.

'Well, you said last week your dad hadn't been well and you'd have to visit them. How was it?'

'Not too bad.'

'I know you find George difficult since his heart attack, but Irene's always pleased to see you.'

'Yes.'

'My father was a bad-tempered old sod too when his heart was playing up, but once he'd had his bypass he was a different person. He was my old Dad again. It's all to do with oxygen not getting to the brain.'

She sighed, unconvinced. 'Mine was a bad-tempered old sod before his heart started playing up. I don't know how Mum's put up with him all these years.'

'I expect living at Hyams House, and having a housekeeper and gardener on hand, might have something to do with it.'

Jane wouldn't be offended by his cynicism. She knew how much he admired her mother – for her practical streak as well as her determination to fight the ageing process.

When he handed his wife her tea and saw she was studying his face, he wondered if he had misjudged.

She seemed to give herself a mental shake.

'I'm sure you're right. I'll go and get dressed.'

She took the tea with her.

He heard her pottering around the bedroom while the bath filled. She was in the bath when the telephone rang.

'Peter, it's Irene. Can I speak to Jane?'

'She's in the bath. Shall I get her to ring you back, or can I take a message?'

'It's George. He's had another heart attack – a bad one this time. I'm ringing from the hospital.'

'That's awful. It happened this morning, did it?'

'Actually, it was yesterday evening. I called, but nobody answered the phone. I remembered you were at a conference, so I didn't try to ring you, but I think there must be something wrong with Jane's mobile.'

'Its battery ran out.' His mind was racing. 'You didn't see her at all yesterday then?'

'We haven't seen her for a week. Why?'

'Oh... only that she was talking about popping in to see you while I was away. What ward is George in?'

'He's in intensive care, but they'll let family in. He may not make it out this time.'

He promised they would be there as soon as Jane was dressed and went up to tell his wife.

Her face was white when he left the bathroom, although neither of them had referred to dinner at Hyams House.

That was a conversation for another day.

~~~

The Towers

Stephen Oliver

"You had dinner at the Towers recently, didn't you?"

I was startled when Duncan Fellows asked me the question. I had been trying to forget that night ever since.

"Wasn't it around the time the police swooped in on a raid," he persisted. I winced again.

"Yes, it was," I replied tersely. "I don't want to talk about it."

He settled himself more comfortably on his barstool and picked up his G&T.

"Now you're really going to have to tell me all about it," he said before taking a sip. He quirked an eyebrow at me.

I grimaced and picked up my Virgin Mary. I used to drink Bloody Maries, but I'm off the booze now. Being drunk makes it harder to forget what happened.

"C'mon," he encouraged me. "It can't have been that bad, can it?"

"You think?" I asked.

It was all coming back to me as if it had only happened last night. I felt it slither into my mind, and I shuddered as I remembered...

~

The Towers had, at one time, been the residence of an eccentric Victorian multimillionaire who made his money in textiles. He had built the house to demonstrate his wealth, and to thumb his nose at the rich who had looked down theirs when he was seeking investors for his new, automated factories.

Personally, I believed that "eccentricity" had shaded over into full-blown insanity.

There were stairways leading up to walls, corridors that only connected to other corridors going nowhere, secret rooms galore, and a living room with everything attached to the ceiling.

And those were the comprehensible parts.

At least two towers appeared to have no entrance, and there were rumours of an extensive set of rooms beyond the wine cellar, although no one had ever found the way in.

When the last of the family line died out, the estate was transferred to the county in lieu of decades of unpaid property taxes. In an attempt to recoup their losses, the authorities remodelled what they could and let parts of it out to artists, writers, and others who followed a creative lifestyle.

Billy Squires was an old school friend: one of those sensitive people unfit for anything like a real job. In his time, he had experimented with aquarelles, oils, charcoal and chalk, poetry, sculpture, and many other things before settling on holographic mobiles.

He had kept in contact with me, of all his former friends from his youth, because I ran my own computer company, providing bespoke software to anyone who needed something out of the ordinary by way of programming. I developed specialised control systems for him, designed to move the hologram plates and lasers in 3D space.

My breakthrough had been to use some of the lasers as sensors to interact with the viewer, making the experience unique to each person. They took into account body form and size, major and micro-movements... even the temperature of the breath as they exhaled, using infrared beams.

He called me one afternoon, full of excitement, and wanted me to come over at once for dinner.

When I arrived, he was waiting in the entrance hall. He grabbed my arm and dragged me up the stairs to his apartment.

He had pizzas and beer already laid out when we entered. He stuffed his face and waited impatiently while I ate, checking his watch every couple of minutes.

"What's the rush?" I asked him.

"I have something I just have to show you," he said.

"Come on," he added as he stood up and headed for the door.

I washed the last of the pizza down with a mouthful of beer and followed him downstairs.

The equipment was set up at one end of the wine cellar. He pulled me behind the laptop controlling the bank of servers that ran everything.

"Watch this," he exclaimed as he started the program.

I noticed that all the sensory lasers were pointing into the corner of the room. The patterns projected from the holograms wandered all over the place at first as they were designed to do when nobody was in the area.

Soon, however, they all began to focus themselves on the corner, overlapping one another, creating a confusion of light and motion.

"What's going on?" I asked Billy. "Why are they all pointing that way?"

"I'm not sure," he replied, "but check this out." He pointed to the display on the laptop.

The screen was showing "motion detection" mode. It was something I'd built in during development, to allow me to monitor the detector lasers and ensure that they were sensing movement correctly. I'd never bothered to remove it before rolling it out. Instead, I'd moved it into the "Extras" menu.

Now, the screen was showing... something – or rather, several somethings – in the corner. I looked up and squinted into the farrago of 3D images in the area, but I couldn't make out anything. There was too much confusion.

I stood and made my way carefully towards the corner, taking care to avoid the sensor lasers, so as not to disturb them.

No matter how careful I was, I still couldn't make out what they were focusing on. It had to be something outside the visible spectrum.

Billy pressed in close behind me.

"Can you see anything?" he asked in a breathless voice.

I remembered that voice from the past. Whenever he thought he was onto something mysterious, he would get excited and speak this way.

"No, nothing," I replied. "It's far too bright. I've got to get closer."

I edged along the wall, keeping my back flat to it, sliding along while I looked ahead. Billy was still close to me.

"Oh my God," he gasped.

For a moment, I couldn't see what he was seeing. It looked like there was a hole in the wall.

The holograms were streaming into it.

"Go on," Billy urged in a quiet voice. "We've got to see where it goes."

"What do you mean?" I whispered back.

"I think this could be the way into the rest of the cellar area. It's supposed to lie under the whole building, not just this corner."

I turned to look at him. "Are you sure?"

"Of course not. But it's certainly leading somewhere."

"We need to be prepared."

He held up a military-grade torch. "I am."

He slid past me and headed into the confusion of light images. I was intrigued enough to follow him.

We were surrounded by the holographic images, half blinding and baffling us, as we pushed through them. I was no longer sure of the direction we were moving in, or how far we had walked.

It wasn't long before we seemed to be moving through endless space, blacker than anything I have ever known, except for the light from the holograms.

Suddenly, Billy stopped in front of me.

"What is it?" I asked him.

"I'm not sure. All I know is, it doesn't look like any of the holograms I created."

I peered over his shoulder.

Whatever it was, it didn't resemble anything like the 3D images I was used to.

It twisted and spun, rotating in more directions than I could imagine, turning inside out in ways I was sure I didn't want to understand.

Despite all this, there was a sense that it was a living being: something existing in far more dimensions than the three I knew.

Slowly, I became aware of sounds. A strange droning numbed my thoughts, like a cacophony of bees, each humming in their own key. Drums, dull and slow, hammered out a rhythm that had no beat to it, my heart thudding in time to them. Mad piping, as of out-of-tune flutes, drove shards of pain through my ears into my brain.

I wanted to scream until my throat was raw... this was something far beyond anything my brain could handle.

Billy was edging forwards, moving slowly in the direction of... whatever this thing was.

I reached a hand out to grab his shoulder and stop him, but he shook me off and continued to move away from me.

Over the maddening droning, drumming, piping, I could hear him babbling.

"Azathoth... the blight at the centre of creation... the bubbling insanity that is the core of all reality... O mindless, demiurge Sultan of Chaos... I come to you..."

I tried one last time to reach him, but he was too far away.

He drifted away into the chaos, while I struggled to move backwards, retracing my steps. I admit I was a coward, but there was no way I could save him, only myself.

At first, I made little progress, each step like lifting my feet from drying cement that dragged me down. Soon, however, I could sense that the... thing was further away than it had been. Either I was finally succeeding in backing away, or it was returning to whichever realm it came from.

But bits of lighted confusion were streaming from it in my direction. Was it trying to draw me, grab me, pull me in? Attempting to attract me into itself?

Finally, I could make out the walls around me. I was back in the basement. I collapsed to the floor and wept in relief before fainting.

The screaming from elsewhere in the building roused me from my stupor.

I realised that the bits that had been chasing me were flitting past and out into the premises. For some reason, they were unable to leave.

It was obvious that the lights were attacking people. I had to do something about it.

The holograms were still all focusing on the "hole", so I assumed that they were keeping it open in some way.

I began smashing the individual plates with my shoe, careless of the glass fragments on the floor cutting into my feet.

The "hole" appeared to be collapsing.

I can't remember what happened next, but witnesses describe a great explosion of light that rocked the whole building, before imploding again.

~

"... So, what happened after that?" Duncan asked me.

"How did the police get involved?"

I downed the last of the Virgin Mary and signalled the barman. He came over to take my order for a double scotch and keep them coming. Staying sober now was no longer an option; drunken oblivion seemed more attractive.

"One of the residents had the presence of mind to call emergency services. He died a moment later, but the screams the dispatcher heard were enough to alert them. Triangulation on the cell towers gave them the address."

I swallowed the whisky in a single gulp, nearly spilling it as my hands trembled for a moment. I signalled for another.

"They didn't find me for a couple of hours, because they were searching upstairs and bringing the victims down. It was only when one of them mentioned the basement that the firemen came downstairs.

"I was buried under much of the equipment, which appeared to have been sucked into the corner where the 'hole' had been. Apart from cuts and bruises, I was uninjured, making me the luckiest man in the place."

"Whatever do you mean?" Duncan signalled for another G&T for himself and a third whisky for me.

"Every single one of them had been... distorted, is the only way I can describe it."

Duncan quirked an eyebrow at me. "Such as?"

"Organs on the outside of the body, but still able to

function properly. Faces turned inside out. Arms where legs should be and vice versa. Heads pushed into stomachs.

"A husband and wife were melded together into a single being, the two halves facing away from one another."

Duncan was getting paler by the second.

"Please, stop," he gasped and drank his new G&T in one gulp. "Those were the dead ones, I presume."

I shook my head. "Nope, they were still alive. But all of them were insane. The authorities took them away, and no one has seen them since. I hope they all died quickly."

I drank the third whisky then decided I had had enough.

"I was the only one unaffected, apparently. I don't know why. When I told them about the 'hole', scientists probed with ground radar and sonar and told me that there was no empty space behind the corner. They reckoned there had never been one."

"And your old friend Billy?" Duncan asked through clenched teeth.

"No sign of him. No one has seen him since." I stood up and walked to the door of the bar.

Once again, I felt something slithering in the back of my mind.

As it looked back through the eye in the nape of the neck, it saw Duncan shakily order a bottle from the barman.

Another piece of chaos sown, it thought to itself. My Master Azathoth will be pleased.

~~~

Dinner at Beachampton Towers

Philip Cumberland

"You had dinner at Beachampton Towers recently didn't you?"

We were sitting in the saloon bar of a country pub, replete with oak beams, low ceiling, large inglenook fireplace, a large log-burning fire and dozing black Labrador. The decor was authentic: original – apart perhaps, that is, from the Labrador, its legs twitching as it dreamed peacefully in front of the fire. The view from the window was spectacular; the pub was near the top of a steep hill overlooking a wide valley. There was a river at the valley bottom. Deciduous trees on the hill opposite were clad in the spectacular red, browns and golds of their autumn finery, a last dramatic show before they were reduced to the nakedness of winter. An unenthusiastic sun was shining, but not making a huge effort in terms of warmth, despite the hour.

Roger Hamilton turned towards me pint in hand; he liked the real ale found in some country pubs. We sat in armchairs by the window, a low dark oak table between us.

The pub was quiet now after the lunchtime rush. A few regulars were chatting, sitting together quietly in a corner. Occasionally laughter or a woman's giggle could be heard above the murmur of quiet conversation.

Roger had asked for the meeting, phoning out of the blue a day or two earlier. We had been at university together, sharing a flat in halls before renting a house with three other lads. Over the years since university, we had lost touch, to a certain extent. He worked for a stockbroker in London, I as a librarian in North Yorkshire. I was unsure as to his current employment, only aware he no longer worked as a stockbroker.

Communications between us took the form of the odd letter, Christmas cards and, when we remembered, birthday cards. As time progressed, we kept in touch irregularly by email. I knew he was married, with two boys. He had bought a large property in the suburbs – a comfortable family home.

Gradually, I had built a career in journalism and writing, part-time at first, then as a reporter for a local paper, eventually moving south to Hertfordshire. My work now was mainly freelance, mostly for one or two London dailies, travelling into town by train when necessary. Other writing consisted of short stories and magazine articles. I had lived with a succession of ladies – one at a time – eventually settling down to village life in a small thatched cottage with Jennifer. We have been together for ten years and are childless.

"Are you writing an article about the dinner?" Roger continued.

"Articles, plural. Three publications: one of the upmarket Sundays, The Courier: three thousand words about Cavendish."

Roger spluttered into his beer at the mention of The Courier.

"Are you still a leftie?" I said. "Pretty strange for an ex-stockbroker, surely?"

"But look at who owns it."

"They pay me well and usually quickly."

"Who else? You said three publications."

"A piece for Top Notch, with pictures – Sam Bryant was the photographer. Celebrity gossip mainly."

"Destined for the ladies hairdressers no doubt. And?"

"The Confidential."

"The Confidential – how are you going to pitch that?"

"Well, for a start, I can't openly use a lot of the stuff I gained. I write under different names for different papers."

"Sebastian Smollett?"

"Yes, in The Confidential."

"Hasn't anyone twigged yet, what you're up to?"

"They might have. Lady Isobel Dove – the precocious fifteen-year-old – she tried to have her photo taken with me. She wasn't overdressed. Saw it coming and dodged out of the way. Her history is well known to me. And the way she has been used by her uncle to blackmail people. She has been active for some time.

"I know where the photos, negatives and files are stored."

"You haven't any yourself?"

I shook my head.

"Not likely. Having those pictures on your hard drive is asking for trouble. Certain people will be told where things are, at the right time."

"So, what went on?"

"They have Cavendish lined up for the next PM. Lady Isobel paid him a lot of attention."

"Did you say anything to Cavendish?"

"Yes – when we were in the Gents I mentioned that Lady Isobel is a remarkably mature young lady for a fifteen-year-old."

"How did that go down?"

"He went rather pale and nipped out as quickly as he could."

"She does look a lot older. What is the line for The Courier?"

"It's a build-up piece for Cavendish; they have him in their pocket and want him as PM. Another beer?"

"Same again, please."

I returned from the bar with a pint for Roger and white wine for myself.

"Are you going all suburban – white wine?"

"Bladder problems."

"Sorry. Who else was there at the dinner?"

"It was ostensibly a Forces charity dinner. They are trying to portray Cavendish as a caring, patriotic man-of-the-people. All the usual suspects were in attendance: two or three members of the cabinet, a couple of retired generals, a second division royal... Admiral Rickett-Howe – he was there."

"What about Proby – I mean Wilkins?"

The name alerted me immediately.

Proby wasn't a name Roger should have knowledge of. My instincts earlier had not let me down.

I made light of the slip.

"Not PJ Proby? He is nothing like Wilkins, Wilkins hasn't got a pony-tail for a start... mind you, if he is still alive he probably hasn't got any hair now. Proby, that is."

"Slip of the tongue. Can't think why I said that."

"Wilkins was there, of course, giving audiences in the library. Every now and again one or other of the worthies would disappear to the library."

"What about Cavendish?"

"Definitely in Wilkins pocket. During his speech he kept glancing up at Wilkins from the notes, seeking approval."

"What are you writing for The Confidential?"

"I am not sure whether to go satirical – money spent feeding the worthies could have been spent looking after ex servicemen; the victims of greed and incompetence by the government, banks and arms manufacturers – or whether to start asking a few awkward questions."

"So what have you got on Wilkins and Cavendish?"

"Footage and audio from the library meetings – loads of the dirt Wilkins has on the great and the good as video footage, photos and financial records."

"How did you manage that?"

"The library – piece of cake. They set up their own surveillance gear; I just hacked into it."

"And the rest of it?"

"Anonymous source for a lot of it – a Jiffy bag by courier, containing some original paperwork, copies of letters, memory sticks and a couple of DVDs."

"Is it safe?"

"I think so. Followed the example of the Stevens enquiry – several duplicate copies of everything are hidden in different locations, all on hold-down. It took me weeks to get everything in place."

"Hold-down?"

"If anything untoward happens to me it all gets released – a lot of it abroad, safe from D-Notices. Some will be published in blogs."

"What are you intending to do?"

"Wilkins is a nasty piece of work, blackmailing members of the government to effectively run the country for his own enrichment. He has control of the politicians and royals, hence the knighthood. He knows their weaknesses and exploits them."

The glasses were empty. Roger stood up.

"I'll get these."

"I'm fine. You have one if you want."

I watched him go to the bar... watched carefully as he collected his new pint and carried it untouched to the table.

"Do you mind if I have that one? Seeing it there has made me thirsty."

"Certainly. I'll get another," he said.

Bugger, I thought. Getting paranoid – not even trusting my oldest friend not to poison me. But there was mention of Proby.

He returned, sitting opposite me in the deep red leather armchair. Lifting his pint.

"Cheers, you were saying..."

"Oh yes, Wilkins must be stopped. He has control of the government and owns most of the media."

Roger stood his pint carefully back down on the beer mat, careful not to mark the table. I sipped my beer, not quite to my taste but palatable, before continuing.

"Cavendish will become prime minister; Wilkins has him set up for the job – favourable press coverage, gushing editorials and the destruction of his rivals. Don't forget, I have seen the plans and the material. Wilkins wants a favourable tax deal and government contracts for his service companies.

"He has enough on Cavendish to ensure it will happen, due, in no small part, to good work by Lady Isobel."

"What then – drop the goods on Wilkins and Cavendish?"

"Timing is crucial, once they have Cavendish in place as PM, they will go for a quick favourable budget. Then, providing the polls are good enough, an early election, hoping for a largish majority."

I sipped my beer. Roger leaned forward to pick up his pint from the table. In doing so his jacket opened revealing fleetingly the handle of a small pistol, visible at the top of the inside pocket.

Now why would Roger need a gun?

It seemed now – more so than originally – a good idea to pick this pub. It was well known to me, and the saloon bar where I had suggested we meet, looked out onto the road outside.

I had phoned earlier that day to change the venue from our original meeting place in town. From a vantage point hidden in the trees on the hill opposite, I had observed Roger through binoculars as he arrived in his black Mercedes sports car and parked it behind the pub.

After making sure he was alone, I drove down to the pub in my old grey Morris Minor, passing by the saloon bar window and waving. I was wearing a flat hat and a brown sheepskin jacket, both of which I left in the car when parking it.

"So will you drop the goods during the campaign?" he continued.

"Very early on. They will have to get someone else in place pretty quick; it will be a resigning matter for Cavendish."

"Who?"

"I don't know, but whoever it is will lose the election."

I set my unfinished beer on the table. "I need to visit the Gents."

"I'll join you."

"I am afraid not, it's a single-seater."

I stood, and made my way to the toilets, passing a conversation in the corner en route.

Jennifer stood up at the table of regulars, announcing she needed to visit the little girls' room. When we were near each other, I slipped her my car keys, and left by the side door.

A few minutes later the Morris Minor trumpeted its way out of the car park and passed the saloon bar window, its driver wearing a sheepskin jacket and flat hat.

Roger rushed out of the front door to the car park. He virtually leapt into his Mercedes, started the engine and set off in pursuit of the Morris Minor.

Satisfying myself the coast was clear, I unlocked and mounted my electric bike, setting off along the cycle track, up the hill and away from the pub. I had left the bike there earlier, leaning against the pub wall, a coat and cycle helmet ready in the panniers. At the top of the hill I rode around the area to ensure the coast was clear before returning home.

Jennifer told me she was parked in a lay-by, standing beside the car when Roger drove past her as she viewed the valley through binoculars. She had removed the sheepskin coat and flat hat and stowed them in the car. Roger slowed down but drove on without stopping.

I hadn't told Roger that a second Jiffy bag had been delivered – this one, with the goods on Proby and Smithson. Roger's name had cropped up in the material but the connections were unclear. It was enough, though, to put me on my guard.

He knows now, as does everyone, that more information had come my way.

Let us hope Mrs Johnson makes a decent fist of things; we could do with a change for the better. I won't be around much longer to find out. The move to a warmer country has only delayed the inevitable, but at least my demise is likely to be from natural causes.

~~~

Decision Day

Wendy Fletcher

Mike put the phone down and ran his hands through his thinning hair.

'You look stressed,' commented Julie who sat at the next desk.

'She's really pushing me now,' sighed Mike, 'saying that today is D for Decision day. Otherwise, it's a big ND for No Deal.'

'Well, we have had her manuscript for four months,' Julie reminded him tentatively, 'Perhaps she has a point.'

'I know, I know,' Mike conceded. 'It's just that it's always such a gamble.'

Julie smiled, 'Everything in this game is a gamble.'

'Yes,' Mike looked weary. 'But with first-time authors, I always feel that I am putting my head on the block. Our reputation as a publishing company depends on me getting it right.'

Julie sat poised, fingers ready to fire off the standard rejection letter. This was part of her job that she did every working day, but always with an awareness that her letter would bring another disappointment, another shattered dream.

'So is that a "no"?

'I'm really not sure.' Mike shook his head.

'Well, what is your gut feeling on this one?' Julie tried to draw him.

'I'm just not sure there's a niche in the market for this kind of stuff but, hey-ho, nothing ventured, nothing gained, as they say.'

'So is that a "yes"?' Julie waited.

'I suppose so.'

Mike picked up the phone again and dialled Amanda in the office next door.

'Hi, Amanda, can you get up the number for Miss Rowling?' and as he waited for the connection he muttered to himself, 'What sort of name is that for a writer? JK Rowling, the reader will never remember that....'

~~~

PUNCHLINES

Think of a joke, and write a story around it

...

Hare Today and Gone Tomorrow.

Caroline Cowan.

Driving along the country lanes with a friend, I was happily enjoying nature at its best, taking in the sights and sounds of the countryside and viewing the wonderful wildlife. The sun was slowly setting and turning everything to a golden hue; it was finally time to make our way home. We drove for many miles with the windows down as it was still warm.

We stopped for a last look around us, to watch hares and rabbits race across the fields and listen to the birds singing the evening chorus before flying off to their nests. Then we slowly drove off leaving them playing their games.

There was a bump! I stopped the car and we both climbed out, not knowing what to expect. Lying in front of me was a hare. I checked it over; it was dead. I sobbed my heart out, knowing I had hit this poor creature and killed it.

It was then that I suddenly remembered the bottle in the boot of the car. I rushed to the back of the car and dug around for it.

"What on earth are you doing?" my friend asked as I sprayed the contents all over the hare.

"Watch and wait," I replied.

Within a few seconds, the hare sprang back to life. It jumped up and hopped down the road, madly waving at us as it went. It looked back many times, still waving.

"Wow," my friend said. "That was a hare-raising experience! How did you do that?"

"Well," I said, "On the back of the bottle it says that the spray lovingly restores life to dead or damaged hair and also gives a permanent wave."

~~~

Together

Cathy Cade

Of all the burrows in all the riverbanks in all the world, she'd taken refuge in his.

The young doe backed in as far as she could. The water-vole felt her tremble. A terrier pup thrust its nose into the hole. It pulled back and began to dig.

When the vole had found this collapsed warren, the earth was still loose and he easily excavated a new home to his own requirements. But his inner tunnel was snake-thin, and the doe was... a rabbit.

The pup stopped digging to stick his nose back in the hole. He was close now. Mud-crusted whiskers pulled back as he prepared to scrabble again, and the vole took his opportunity. He darted from the burrow and up the riverbank.

Easily diverted, the puppy scampered after him along the towpath until he veered into undergrowth. The dog snuffled around the verge as the vole doubled back to his burrow.

In his underground antechamber, the doe still crouched, trembling. He had watched this one with her litter-mates when they first emerged from their warren further along the river. He had gone there to forage among the shoots of seeds blown from the field at seed-time. After the seedlings were gone he still went back to worship from afar.

He didn't understand what it was that drew him from the safety of his own territory. Smaller than the other kits, her luxuriant fur, magnificent ears, and dark, shining eyes were different from the female voles whose nests he guarded. He should be programmed to desire their tiny ears and button eyes, but instead he was captivated by this elegant doe.

He entered his burrow and crept to her side. She was far above him but, for now, they were together. He felt her warmth and listened to her heartbeat steadying. The soft fur of her flank mingled with his as they watched side-by-side.

Together.

He could have stayed like that forever.

She made a tentative move to the burrow's mouth and her nose twitched in that way that made his heart flip. He joined her at the mouth of the burrow. They scanned the riverbank and towpath together.

The bank was clear now, and the air was calm, but she seemed in no hurry to leave. Together, they basked in the quiet warmth of the afternoon as the river chuckled past.

A buck rabbit appeared from the cornfield and sat up to survey his surroundings. Catching sight of the doe, he moved a length closer. She stretched to return his gaze and the buck lolloped toward her. She hopped to the towpath and stopped to look back, her eyes soft with gratitude and – could it be? – affection.

The buck approached her and stopped.

Along the riverbank, a dog barked. The rabbits leapt together and – together – were gone.

The vole slipped back through his snaking burrow, to curl up in his nest and relive his memories.

Briefly, he had worshipped at her feet, knowing that his extravagant dreams could never be fulfilled, knowing from the start that a vole and his bunny are soon parted.

~~~

Harry

Stephen Oliver

Harry the Hare was playing one of his pranks again.

He was much flightier than his brother and sisters, or even his cousins. In fact, pretty much everyone in Fairyland despised him and his antics.

It was only his size that protected him. Most fairies only came up to his nose tip.

He had been lying in wait for a couple of hours now, the massive carrot ready to tip over into the pile of mud and splash anyone who might be walking by.

He heard cheering and shouting approach, telling him that a large group of fairies, elves and sprites were coming down the path.

He crouched lower and put his shoulder to the carrot, ready to push.

He could see the movement of all the figures through the bushes as he shoved. The carrot crashed through the vegetation, hit the mud, and sprayed it in all directions. Cries of disgust and anger erupted as he bounded away.

Nobody saw him, but he heard several voices crying his name.

"Haaaarrrrrryyyyyy!"

He grinned to himself on the way home, happy that his latest practical joke had succeeded so well.

That evening, there was a knock on the door.

He delayed answering it because he was taking the first of a new batch of lettuce and carrot tarts out of the oven. They smelled so wonderful that he couldn't help nibbling one

The knocking got louder.

"Okay, okay, I'm coming," he called as he hopped down the corridor.

Standing outside was a pretty little fairy with sky blue wings. She showed him a jewelled badge.

"Fairyland Bureau of Investigation, Senior Field Agent Periwinkle Bluebell," she identified herself. "May I come in?"

"Of course, if you don't mind talking to me in the kitchen. I have some baking I need to keep an eye on."

In the kitchen, Harry turned to the fairy.

"What does the FBI want with me," he asked.

"You know, Harry," she replied. "You've been warned about your japes and jokes before, but today you went too far. You splattered mud and crud all over Queen Titania's new robes. It will take weeks to clean them, and she wanted to wear them to the Midsummer's Ball tomorrow evening."

Harry shrugged philosophically.

"Shit happens."

"Yes, but you've been doing too much of this shit recently. The queen has sent me with a final warning. If you don't mend your ways, she will have all the magicians of the Seelie Court cast a spell on you and turn you into a goon."

She took a breath to continue her tirade but was interrupted by a lettuce and carrot tart flying through the air, smacking her in the face.

"Harry," she spluttered as she wiped the orange and green filling out of her eyes, "you were warned. Tomorrow morning, they will cast the spell. What do you think of that?"

Harry was philosophical.

"That's life," he said. "Hare today, goon tomorrow."

~~~

Vespidae Acoustic

Val Chapman

Raymond Harper had always appeared to be slightly 'odd'. If he had been born a few decades later he would, in all probability, have been diagnosed as being on the autistic spectrum. But little was known about the condition in 1947 when Raymond's parents were struggling to understand their only son.

As it was, a few of his acquaintances had guessed 'Aspergers'. Others just dismissed him as weird.

His parents indulged his childish obsessions, when he would focus all his time and energy into a favoured topic such as snakes, aeroplanes or – for an exhausting four months – mountaineering.

None of these obsessions lasted for long but, for the time Raymond was interested in them, they were all-consuming. When he developed an interest in wasps at the age of eight, something 'clicked'. The more he delved into their lives and habits, the more intrigued he became.

He supposed he saw something of himself in the behaviour of wasps – in the solitary single-mindedness of their activities. Very few people were interested in them, or even appeared to like them very much, but Raymond felt an affinity with the little creatures.

He was academically gifted and easily followed that well-worn path of school, college and university, earning himself accolades for his work with, and about wasps. European wasps were his speciality.

Pedantic by nature, Raymond referred to them by the Latin term – vespidae.

His knowledge on the subject was renowned, and his fascination with vespidae never diminished. For nearly three decades, he was acknowledged as the leading expert in all aspects of the European wasp.

While on a lecture tour of Australia, Raymond encountered a fellow wasp fan, and they struck up quite a friendship, trading knowledge and information about their shared passion.

So when Raymond was informed that his friend and colleague had produced a recording of wasp noises he felt more excitement than he had in years.

Not wanting to wait for the record to be sent from Australia, Raymond headed straight to the record shop on the day of its release.

"I believe there is a record released today – 'European Vespidae Acoustics'. Do you have it?"

"Indeed, we do sir, would you care to listen to it?" replied the assistant.

Raymond didn't need to be asked twice.

Picking up headphones, he almost quivered with anticipation.

The assistant carefully placed the needle on the first

track. Raymond listened for a few seconds and removed the headphones.

"Excuse me," he said. "There may have been a mistake. I don't recognise these sounds."

"I'm sorry, sir," the assistant said. "Let's try again."

The needle was lowered onto the record for the second track.

"No, no, this isn't right either. I am the leading expert in the European wasp, and I tell you I have never heard these sounds before."

The assistant assured Raymond that the record was indeed the correct one, and they agreed to try once more. This time, Raymond listened intently for a few more seconds before throwing down the headphones, fuming.

"These are not the sounds of European wasps I can assure you."

The manager of the shop heard the commotion and came over to where his assistant was trying to calm Raymond down. He took charge of the situation and, looking at the album, quickly grasped the problem.

He turned to Raymond.

"I'm terribly sorry, sir, it appears we have been playing you the bee side."

~~~

Wanted

Valerie Fish

It was quite a shock seeing his own face staring back at him like that, but he really should have seen it coming.

Ron was only five feet tall, or five feet short he'd say (at least he could laugh about himself), but what he lacked in stature he made up for in personality. He certainly was a larger-than-life character; his mother used to say he could charm the hind legs off a donkey.

It was those charms that led him into his lucrative side-line. His day job at the office bored him to tears and paid a pittance but, come the evenings, he would have the ladies hanging on his every word.

All he did was tell them what they wanted to hear. If his 'messages from the other side' made them happy, who was he to argue? They were more than happy to hand over their money, having heard from their dearly departed (or so they thought). It wasn't difficult doing the research beforehand. They were so gullible – not realising that they were feeding him the information themselves and he was simply giving it back to them! They fell for it hook, line and sinker every time.

All was going well for Ron until the day he heard rumblings that the local paper were doing a feature on fake mediums and a reporter had been doing some fishing. Apparently, his name had been mentioned as one of the phonies.

It was time to lie low for a while.

Some weeks later, Ron hadn't heard any more and was beginning to think it had all come to nothing. Nevertheless, he was reluctant to open his local paper, for fear of what he would find.

On the other hand, he needed to know: had he been rumbled?

His answer was at the newsagents. He didn't need to go inside; the sign was there for all to see.

WANTED

SMALL MEDIUM AT LARGE

~~~

Wind-up Wedding

Jan Cunningham

Ron sat at the kitchen table tapping a biro on his teeth.

"What are you writing Dad?" asked his daughter Judy. "You never write anything, not even a shopping list."

"I'm going to write my wedding speech," he replied.

"Da-ad," said Judy warningly, "Don't you dare. I know what you're like and I don't want it. This is *my* day. Can't you just be normal for once? DO NOT embarrass me in front of everyone with your jokes, especially the ones at my expense. Just get up, thank everyone, etc, etc, then raise a toast to me and Dave and sit down again. We'll have enough of that sort of thing from the best man, thank you very much."

"Oh come on love, be a sport. Course I'm going to embarrass you, that's what dads do," said Ron with a wicked twinkle in his eye.

"I will never forgive you if you ruin the best day of my life!" came the angry retort and Judy stomped out the door, slamming it behind her.

"Oh, leave it out, love, will you? Please," begged his wife Ann. "She's got enough on her plate with her wedding arrangements without you winding her up every two minutes. She so wants it to be perfect that she's getting herself into a right state about it."

"I know," Dave replied, "but I can't resist it. It's so easy."

And it was. Over the weeks leading up to the wedding Ron persisted in telling his daughter all the tales he was going to put in his speech...

About the time Granny had taken a fancy to the table decoration in the restaurant – a cloth snail. "And when we got outside you opened your handbag and there it was. You'd nicked it for her.

"Or the time you were coming home from college and were going to buy a ticket on the train, as you hadn't had time to get one before, but you saw the ticket collector coming just as the train was pulling into Peterborough, so you kept moving down the carriages ahead of him, jumped off as soon as, and had a free trip home."

Judy rose to the bait every time; she just couldn't help herself. Her nerves were frazzled, worrying if the flowers and buttonholes would arrive on time; if the place seatings were right, with no-one sitting by the wrong person; if her dress and the bridesmaids' would be finished on time... and a million other worries. Her dad's constant joking and reading out bits of his speech made her angry and frightened. She couldn't trust him not to say those things.

Ron had a reputation as a joker. On Friday nights in the pub with his mates, he kept them roaring with laughter as he recounted tales about people he knew. He exaggerated and added to the tales to make them funnier, but often this was at the other person's expense. He got away with it because he was good at it, and nobody wanted to give him the satisfaction of appearing upset, as this would've made things even worse. But it could seem a bit cruel at times.

The wedding had gone without a hitch so far. Ron stood up and announced to present company that it was time to give his father-of-the-bride speech.

"Ladies, Gentlemen, and anyone else who managed to get past the guard dogs on the door, otherwise known as my sons, thank you all for coming today to celebrate the shotgun wedding of my daughter Judy to Dave." (Polite laughter.)

"Judy is the light of my life. After three healthy rumbustious lads her mum and I were delighted to be given a 'sugar and spice and all things nice' baby girl. And Judy was just such a girl – pretty (demanding), loving (especially when she wanted something), and good-natured (until you upset her and then, boy, stand back and watch the fireworks).

"I remember only too well her brothers and I trying to initiate Judy into the delights of cricket. She was *not,* sadly, a natural. Bowling was not her strength but, boy, she could hurl down some mean overarm chucks so we nicknamed her 'Ferocious Fanny.'

"And another time, when she was in her 'can't be bovvered' phase, she sent back a blank exam paper, with only a poem on the back."

Ron glanced sideways at his daughter and was taken aback by the anger in her eyes and a shine that heralded tears.

"Well, Ladies and Gentlemen, as I am under strict orders to keep my speech short and sweet and not to embarrass my daughter any further, I will do as I'm told for a change.

"Those of you who know me know that I'm a dab hand in the kitchen. So I thought, on this very special day, I would give you all my very own, never before revealed, recipe for marriage.

"Feel free to take notes.

"First, ingredients.

"Take a large dollop of love (you can never have too much of this so be generous), a big helping of laughter (problems don't seem half as bad if you laugh at them), with large tablespoons of kindness, understanding, and thoughtfulness. Throw in a listening ear, and add generous pinches of give and take. Mix them all thoroughly together and cook slowly for a lifetime.

"It will not go stale or mouldy if you just give a top up of surprises every now and then."

Then Ron tipped his glass to his wife, smiled and said, "And here's one I made earlier.

"Ladies and Gentlemen, without more ado I give you a toast to my beautiful daughter and the rogue she has married, God help him.

"Judy and Dave."

~~~

Pemrose and Quilp

Philip Cumberland

Pemrose and Quilp are a comedy-writing organisation, established as a co-operative some time ago. Few are aware even of their existence; no one knows when they appeared but nobody can remember a time when they weren't there.

The offices of Pemrose and Quilp are within one of the Cambridge colleges, I am not permitted to disclose which one. On arrival, I was directed by the porter to a substantial oak door in a corner of the quadrangle to my far left. Although narrow, the door would not have been out of place on a church. Screwed to the door was a polished brass plate, whilst on the door frame an ostentatious bell push caught the eye. The plate read, "Pemrose and Quilp. Please knock." Instead, I pressed the bell.

"Can't you read?" said a voice.

"Probably a tourist," replied another voice.

"They let anyone in these days you know," continued voice number one.

The door was opened by an attractive young lady wearing a black academic gown over a tweed business suit. The conversation stopped as the door opened; a speaker was attached to the door frame.

"Good morning, Mr?"

"Jason Grimsby. I have an appointment."

"With whom?"

"Mr Pemrose and Mr. Quilp."

"Follow me – although Mr Pemrose said your name was Jacob Hull."

I followed the young lady – a pleasure in itself – as she led me along a stone-walled corridor, punctuated at intervals by oak doors on both sides. Some doors sported brass plaques, worn thin from years of polishing, the wording faint. I read *Punchlines* on one, *Openings* on another. At the end of the corridor, the young lady opened a door and ushered me into a large room. An old man sitting at one of two ancient oak desks looked up.

"Mr. Grimsby for you, Mr. Pemrose and Mr. Quilp."

"Thank you Miss Holmes," said Mr. Pemrose as he rose stiffly from his desk. "Has the script for the BBC been despatched?"

"Wilton Crabapple?"

"Yes, that's the one."

"I sent it by courier earlier, sir."

"Thank you, Miss Holmes."

Miss Holmes withdrew and Mr. Pemrose came from behind his desk. Mr Quilp also stood and joined us. Mr Pemrose offered me a wrinkled hand, "Oliver Pemrose, and this is Grantly Quilp."

Both men, despite their advanced years, had firm handshakes; it would be several minutes before the blood flow returned to my hand.

"Take a seat, Mr. Hull – sorry, Grimsby," said Mr. Quilp indicating a large red leather armchair in a corner of the room, one of three. The two men joined me and we sat with a low table of heavy dark oak between us. The room was sparsely furnished, with walls of undecorated bare stone. Three leaded glass stone-framed windows occupied one wall overlooking the quadrangle. The door I had entered and a large ancient black cast iron radiator graced another. On a third wall hung an oil painting of Oliver Cromwell, warts and all. To one side of it an oak bookcase, filled with a selection of volumes ancient and modern, reached nearly to the ceiling. In the corner between this and the fourth wall, which featured another door, was a complete standing skeleton. Seeing me eye the skeleton, Mr. Pemrose spoke.

"Our clients all know the office is manned at the weekends and evenings by a skeleton crew; we call him Charlie." I swear the skeleton inclined its head in acknowledgement.

Mr Pemrose continued, "Now, Mr. Grimsby, you said in your letter you wanted to interview us for an article you are writing about comedy; is that correct?"

"Yes, I would appreciate your help."

"How did you find out about us?" asked Mr. Quilp.

"It wasn't easy," I said. "There were whispers of your names but no mention anywhere in writing. You use pen names for most of your work and have had an enviable range of contributors collaborating with you."

"Yes there is a rich pool of talent within the city. Many move on to careers in their own right; some work here. Others work freelance for us. We function as a co-operative."

Miss Holmes re-entered the room carrying a large tray bearing cups, saucers, sugar, milk, a coffee jug, spoons and a plate of biscuits.

As she set the tray on the table she said, "You had some calls, Mr. Pemrose – the D.G. of the BBC, the Prime Minister and–"

Pemrose interrupted, "Frightful woman – I can't stand her. Still, what can you expect from Oxford? What did you tell them?"

I am sure Charlie nodded in agreement as did Quilp.

"I said you would phone them back later. Spike Milligan rang too."

"I'll ring him back; it will be important. Where is he now? I know he was fed-up with Ireland."

"In the Caribbean I think, sir."

"Could you serve the coffee please, Miss Holmes? Would you excuse me, Mr. Grimsby? I won't be long."

"Are you teaching today, Miss Holmes?" asked Quilp

"I have a lecture at 4pm and then tutorials so I am off at three. Mrs Mehew will take over until six."

"Thank you, Miss Holmes."

Mr Pemrose left the room. Miss Holmes served the coffee before following him. As we sipped, I turned to Mr. Quilp. "I thought Spike Milligan was dead."

"Don't believe everything you read in the papers, young man, even if you write it yourself. He had a lot of woman trouble; his 'death' put a stop to that. He shaved off his beard, got a decent haircut, consulted a doctor we know and is a changed man. He looks healthier now, and younger. Of course, he made prudent financial arrangements before his demise."

I looked at the painting of Cromwell. "Is that an original?"

"Yes, by Samuel Cooper. Mr. Cromwell donated it when he gave us these rooms, as a thank-you."

"A thank-you?"

"At the start of the Civil War the college silver was on its way to the Royalists. They were ambushed, and the silver recovered for the Parliamentarians. We arranged the ambush and stopped the silver getting into the wrong hands."

Charlie nodded approvingly – that skeleton definitely moved.

Pemrose bounced back into the room. "Spike sends his regards."

"Have you sorted him out?" asked Quilp.

"He sorted himself out really. I just nudged him in the right direction. He is in the Caribbean at the moment romantically entwined with a Jamaican lady, he says."

"Silly old sod – you'd think he would know better at his age."

Pemrose picked up his waiting coffee; Quilp refilled my cup and his own.

"How is the interview going?" asked Pemrose.

"We haven't got very far." replied Quilp. "Anyone want a biscuit?" We each took a plain chocolate digestive from the plate.

"I was telling him about Mr. Cromwell and the college silver," said Quilp.

"Ah yes, splendid fellow. I wonder how he would have got on with Newton?"

"We have discussed this before; it would certainly have been interesting."

"I think Newton would have changed Cromwell. Newton's research on the Trinity was incontrovertible, and Cromwell admired the truth."

"How do think Cromwell would have dealt with it?"

"Badly to start with. Newton's arrogance wouldn't help," continued Pemrose. "After a while, Cromwell would see that the truth had been revealed to him and he would look more to himself than to finding divine inspiration."

"Fascinating though this is gentlemen…" I began.

"Don't worry, Mr. Grimsby. Enjoy your coffee. Have another biscuit," continued Pemrose. "The interview is typed up for you already. Miss Holmes has sorted it out – the one you will publish, that is. It has all the anecdotes, jokes and punchlines you need. We have, after all, been in the business a long time."

The interview was – as you know – as good as they promised: conducted in their modern offices at a Science Park on the outskirts of the city. It was witty, funny and engaging, holding the reader's attention throughout. A fortyish Jonathon Quilp and a slightly older Andrew Pemrose look up from their desks in the colour photographs that feature in the article. Charlie – Jonathon Pemrose's handsome black Labrador – appears in many of the photos, as does Miss Jones, wearing a smart tweed suit but no gown.

Yes, there are offices in a Science Park on the outskirts of Cambridge bearing the name of Pemrose and Quilp. It is staffed by the trio in the article and the Labrador. I have been there.

Some of the best comedy originates from Pemrose and Quilp. Much of the rest also comes from Pemrose and Quilp, but not in their name. In the article Pemrose is asked if he has a favourite joke. He replies, "Probably the guide dog joke.

"A man is asked to look after his mother-in-law's-poodle. He decides to take it for a walk. Whilst out walking, he passes a pub and fancies a pint. On the door is a notice, 'No dogs allowed. Guide dogs only'.

He pulls out his sunglasses and puts them on. With the dog, he gropes his way to the bar and orders a pint. The landlord says to him, 'No dogs allowed.'

'It's my guide dog.'

'Guide dogs are usually Labradors or Alsatians,' replied the barman.

'What have they given me then?'"

~~~

This was a joke I heard on Radio 4 some years ago, told by Peter White, a blind radio presenter

.

Joseph's Girl

Wendy Fletcher

Joseph leaned on the gate and watched his daughter leading her pony up the lane towards the farmhouse. His eyes didn't blink; his heart was full of pride. She was a beautiful young woman of eighteen now, with golden curling hair and eyes as blue as the cornflowers that grew in the meadow where the pony had been grazing. He savoured the moment but knew it wouldn't last. It never did. All too soon, he felt that familiar fear strike at the bottom of his stomach: that old enemy that always attacked him at these most precious moments.

Why is she so different from the others?

The question leapt into his head again. For eighteen years, this question had haunted him; he knew it intimately now. He recognised it as if it were an old friend. It hung in the summer air as he worked outside. It hovered by the fireside when he settled in the armchair after a long day. It even joined him under the rough blankets as he closed his eyes for the night. He could feel its approach, yet he had never found a way to block its arrival.

Even today, on this lovely sunny afternoon, it took hold of his heart threatening to choke the love out of it.

Then the guilt grasped him. This was always the sequence, a main course of doubt followed by a generous helping of guilt pudding. He hated himself; his self-loathing drained all pleasure from the moment. He could no longer bear to watch Lucille as she raised an arm in greeting so he turned away and headed back into the house.

The guilt engulfed him now. He knew he should have left when he first saw her before she was aware of his presence. Now he had let her see him turn away, and he knew this would have raised the old question in her mind again too.

Why did he always distance himself from her?

He skulked in the corner of the kitchen, berating himself for being such a coward, until he heard the hoofs of the pony cross the cobbles. He knew Lucille was safely ensconced in the stable, busy for the next half-hour with settling Daisy. Then he crept out of the back door and across the yard to the woodpile. They did need wood chopping. With three coal fires to take the chill off the rambling old house, even in summer, they always needed wood. He could justify to himself the decision to wield the axe today if not perhaps the ferocity with which he brought it down on the seasoned logs.

All days were not this bad, he convinced himself as the sweat ran down his back and soaked the shoulders of his shirt. Today he had been caught out at a weak moment. Mostly he battled the demons with no-one being aware that his thoughts were troubled. He had learnt to hide his feelings well – after all, eighteen years was a long time to practise any skill.

He thought back to the first time he held Lucille in his arms. Was that when the doubt was born?

Yes, she was different even then. She had been tiny and fragile with that golden hair so unlike the boys. They all had dark hair, straight and spiky, all five of them.

For the millionth time he ran this old footage through his mind. Was it the hair? Was it the eyes? Was it the fact that she was so delicate? He remembered how she struggled to feed, how the nurse was concerned that she didn't seem to be 'thriving', as they called it back then. This was all so different from the boys. Each of them in turn had burst into the world raring to go. They would be the strapping sons who would work hard on the farm and one day inherit it, just as Joseph had.

At the time, he had tentatively mentioned these differences and tried to believe the answers.

'Girls are always smaller and weaker.'

'Boys are always more robust.'

'You mark my words, when she's a bit older she will be boss of all them boys.'

He had smiled and nodded but time had not proved them right. Lucille had grown, if anything, more noticeably different. Because she was tiny and sickly, he had felt protective and overwhelmed by his love for her.

As the years passed, and she became more sensitive to his moods he had compensated, some might say over-compensated, by indulging her every whim. That was how Daisy had arrived at the farm in time for her sixteenth birthday.

There were times – so many times – when he had wrestled with the urge to speak his fears out loud, but he couldn't get the words right. How do you choose the moment to say to your wife of nearly thirty years, 'By the way, I was wondering if I am Lucille's father?'

The idea sounded ludicrous even to him when he rehearsed it in his head, so he had pushed the doubts to the back of his mind and concentrated on being the best father he could be to all his children.

Now, though, as he swung that axe, he knew that his thoughts, however irrational, were affecting his relationship with Lucille. She had seen him turn away unable to bear the pain. He knew how selfish that was. It would cause her pain because she didn't know why.

For the first time in her life, the balance changed in his mind. He had to know. He didn't know how he would deal with the blow if his fears had foundation but maybe they could get past it. Perhaps he could accept that Margaret had been lonely. After all, they had lived on this isolated farm for the whole of their marriage and she had spent a lot of time there on her own with the boys when they were small. He had been off to distant markets looking for the best breeds to improve their stock, sometimes staying away for a couple of nights at a time.

His thoughts were becoming quieter. He had stopped swinging between the need to know and the dread of knowing. He would talk calmly to Margaret, plead with her for honesty, assure her that he understood, that it would not affect their marriage or the farm or the boys but it would enable him to be honest with Lucille and build a relationship with her that was not marred by all this uncertainty.

He knew he had made the right decision as soon as he reached it. Now he just wanted to get it over, but he knew he must choose his moment carefully. The boys were all going on a camping trip with friends from school, a sort of reunion, at the end of July and that would be a good chance to talk to Margaret while the house was quiet and they could both spend some time with Lucille afterwards as she came to terms with this shocking news.

Even as he planned this, he knew he had come to terms with it. He was thinking of how he could best help Lucille get over her shock. It wouldn't be a shock to him any more; he had already rationalised it.

The demons would be silenced forever. The doubts and fears would no longer creep into his bed at night or leap out at him on a summer afternoon when Lucille was walking her pony back from the meadow. Now that the end of all this unease was in sight, he was actually looking forward to it.

The best laid plans, however, never go unchallenged. It was the Saturday teatime before the boys left on Sunday. Margaret was busy baking in the kitchen and Lucille was in the living room, sprawled across the armchair, feet dangling over one arm, chatting on the phone to a girl who lived on a farm half a mile up the lane. They sometimes caught the weekly bus and went into town together. Joseph heard her voice as he came into the room.

'I'll just make sure getting back later than normal is okay. I'm sure the oldies won't mind as long as you're sure your brother can pick us up.'

Then she put her hand over the mouthpiece and yelled, 'Dad'.

Joseph caught his breath. His face crumpled and his shoulders sagged.

The tears poured down his cheeks and he couldn't speak. Lucille was at his side with one spring over the arm.

'Oh, Dad, what is it? Are you ill? Mum, come quickly. Quickly – I think Dad's having an attack.'

Margaret didn't come. She had realised that she was one egg short for a cake she was baking for tea before the boys left next evening. She had popped to the barn hoping that one of their thirty hens had laid another egg since she collected them at first light.

It was just Joseph and Lucille, and now he saw fear in her eyes. He knew it had to be said now, no more practise, no more rehearsal. She needed reassurance right now.

'It's all okay,' He held out his trembling arms to her. 'Don't panic. I'm not ill. I just feel a bit emotional.'

'A bit? Dad, you're shaking.'

'Lucille, I wasn't going to say this to you until I had spoken to your mum but I think I might not be your Dad. You deserve an explanation. I've never treated you quite right. I want all this resolving once and for all, so we all know where we stand.

'I convinced myself that I could cope with it whatever the answer, but when you called out, the thought that I might never hear you say that again just knocked me over.'

'Oh Dad,' Lucille hugged him to her, 'Don't worry. You see things like this on the telly all the time. As long as you can forgive Mum if she made a bad call all those years ago we'll all be fine and carry on like nothing's changed. You will always be my Dad.'

'I will talk to your mum tonight; this can't be left any longer.'

'We will talk to Mum right this minute.'

Lucille was on her feet with all the determination of a teenager with a mission. Joseph wasn't quick enough to stop her as she strode through to the kitchen, or perhaps he wasn't trying hard enough.

'Well?' Lucille stood over Margaret who sunk onto a kitchen chair. 'What's the story?'

'Have I got a different father from all the boys?'

Margaret sobbed into the tea cloth, her head bent so low they could only see the top of her head.

She nodded.

'Then might I ask who my father is?'

Joseph was hanging on to Lucille's hand as Margaret nodded towards him.

She found her voice just long enough to whisper, 'He is.'

~~~

BEACHES

...

Tide Line

Philip Cumberland

The sea had gone from the beach and was way out in the distance. Debris washed up by the departed tide lay undisturbed. In the early spring morning, an old man walked slowly along the beach. The sand was damp below the tide line, dark and smooth. Amongst plastic bottles, driftwood, seaweed and the odd broken flip-flop left by the departed sea, something unexpected lay on the sand.

Old Bob was shocked at first, and then saddened. A small, sandy coloured, collarless dog lay on its side; the limp body wet and cold to the touch. Thinking the dog dead, the man considered dragging its body higher onto the beach, further above the high water mark, before alerting the authorities.

It was a miracle the gulls had not found it.

While Bob was wondering how he could prevent them attacking the animal, an eye flickered. It opened momentarily and immediately reclosed as if the effort had exhausted the animal. As Bob considered this new information, the eye opened again and looked directly at him, seeming to plead for help.

Instinctively, he unzipped his old brown bomber jacket, scooped up the cold wet body against his own and re-zipped the jacket round him – for he now knew the animal to be male.

The lolling head was all that was visible of the dog. Bob's appearance was strange now, a distended stomach having appeared where before there was little to see. His gait was ungainly as he made his way along the beach bearing his precious cargo. Water from the dog found its way through his jumper and tee-shirt, chilling him.

A milky sun had edged up from the sea and was trying to break through the veil of low cloud. It gave little warmth. He left the beach and walked across the promenade towards a caravan that sold drinks and snacks on the other side of the sea wall, close to the car park. The van was closed at this early hour but there was a tap beside it for bathers to wash sand from their feet or fill bottles and kettles. Fumbling in his pockets, he found a clean handkerchief to hold under the tap. When it was thoroughly soaked, he held it under the nose of the dog's drooping head, urging him to lick the damp cloth. A pale tongue appeared and, as the dog opened his mouth, Bob managed to squeeze drops of water into its mouth. He repeated this exercise a few times then decided it best to get home as quickly possible.

Bob thought of taking the dog home in the basket of his bicycle – an old Post Office delivery bike. As well as carrying home beach finds, he used it for shopping and for journeys too short to require his bus pass. Home wasn't far though, and the dog had to be kept warm. The walk to his bungalow didn't take long despite the awkward bundle. He and his wife had moved to this coastal village when he retired, having sold their urban house to realise their dream of seaside retirement.

Alzheimer's had robbed Bob of the woman he loved long before she died. During the last months in the care home, she didn't recognise him, locked into memories of her childhood. Her death had brought with it the mixed emotions that come with losing a loved one: relief that her suffering was over, mingling with the unimaginable pain of grief and the loneliness of ultimate separation.

He unlocked the door and walked through to the kitchen, still with the dog inside his jacket; it seemed warmer now. A salty seaweed smell wafted up through the opening in the jacket from the dog's damp coat.

He hunted around the house to find clean towels and heaped them on the floor with a cushion taken from a kitchen chair. The jacket was unzipped, and the limp, damp, now shivering dog, was lain gently onto the towels.

Bob filled the kettle, switched on and found a hot water bottle, As the kettle warmed, Bob filled a casserole dish with cold water and set it down by the dog. He filled the hot water bottle with warm water and pushed it under the towels, using one to rub the salty moisture from the dog's coat and covering him with a tea towel afterwards since his towel supply was nearly exhausted. He tried filling a turkey baster with water from the casserole dish and squirting a few drops at a time into the dog's mouth. It seemed more aware now, its eyes opening more often and staying open for a few seconds, before closing again, as if the effort took all his energy.

"I bet you're hungry boy, aren't you?" said Bob rising awkwardly from the floor. At the back of the food cupboard, he found a pack of four tins of tuna – it was either that or a tin of stewed steak. The struggle to remove the ring-pull lid reminded him why the tuna was still in the back of the cupboard. The contents were tipped into a cereal bowl. Bob settled himself back onto the hard floor beside the dog, picked up a chunk of fish and held it under the dog's nose. Reluctantly at first, the dog sniffed Bob's fingers. Then the pale tongue flicked out of his mouth and licked the fingers, tasting the oily fish with more interest. The dog was still weak but obviously hungry, so Bob fed him a small amount of tuna by hand.

Bob spent the rest of the day in much the same way, popping out briefly to recover his bike whilst the dog was asleep, having first refreshed the water in the hot water bottle. He collected fish and chips on his way home then returned to his vigil, surprisingly hungry. Pulling up a kitchen chair before sitting down, he devoured his lunch directly from the paper wrapping, washed down with a mug of tea.

The dog did not stir for several hours. It appeared to dream as it slept, occasionally moving its front legs as if swimming, and producing at times a pitiful subdued whimper. Whenever the dog roused sufficiently Bob would feed him water and tuna.

Fearful of losing this new-found acquaintance he maintained his vigil and, as the day passed, the dozing, exhausted dog warmed, its breathing becoming regular and seeming more normal.

Bob must have dozed and was awakened by something wet on his fingers. He opened his eyes. It was dark outside, the kitchen lit only by the light of the television screen. The dog sat swaying by his feet, licking at his fingers. Bob was overjoyed.

The dog made its way unsteadily to the door and looked up at the door handle.

"I expect you want a wee, young fella," said Bob, opening the door.

The dog tottered into the small back garden, staying outside just long enough to empty his bladder before returning, exhausted again, to his makeshift bed.

Bob spent the next few days nursing the dog, now named Flotsam, back to health. Once dry and clean Flotsam was identifiable as possibly a Terrier-Collie cross. After three days Bob felt confident enough to take the bus to the next town to buy Flotsam a collar and lead, leaving the dozing dog shut in the kitchen.

Funds were tight. His wife's funeral had been a financial as well as an emotional drain. He reported Flotsam's arrival to the police, who were happy for him to remain with Bob, unless someone reported him missing.

The vet who examined Flotsam a few days later couldn't find a microchip, so fitted him with one. The kindly vet vaccinated him very cheaply, keen to help out the poor pensioner who had adopted him.

After a while, Flotsam was shortened to Sam.

Sam would occupy most of the basket on Bob's old Post Office bike as they rode around the village and surrounding countryside.

Most days, the two of them go beachcombing, the time of their visits changing with the tides. Although they one day made a discovery that solved Bob's financial problems for life, he always felt that his most precious find had been Sam.

~~~

On the Beach

Val Chapman

Amanda watched her daughter playing in the sand.

The sun, though barely there, was enough to highlight Leyla's fine hair, giving it a look of spun gold, and the appearance of a halo.

Appropriate, Amanda thought, for her little angel.

The beach was quiet, especially where they were, at the base of the cliffs just beyond the rock pools. Amanda was pleased; she needed some peace to collect her thoughts after these recent weeks, and to spend some time with her daughter.

She had made her way down to the beach, over the large, smooth pebbles giving way to smaller, sharper stones, then onto the long stretch of pale, buff-coloured sand, perfect for building sandcastles. It was a pretty beach in its own way, but Amanda was more interested in the stretch of sand beyond the rock pools.

It was here she sat, calmly watching her beautiful little girl looking for pieces of sea glass and interesting shells, with her delicate, long-fingered hands.

Pianist hands, her grandmother called them. She swore she would be famous one day, for a skill no one else in the family possessed. Her mother, though, had always said that Leyla's hands were made for diamonds.

Amanda thought she liked that idea better.

It was all immaterial now though, she thought, gazing at her adored daughter. A freak accident at the beach had taken Leyla from her. It was taking so much time for Amanda to realise that she would never hold her beautiful baby again, never breathe her in anymore, her skin always smelling faintly of candy-floss, for some inexplicable reason.

Here though, was one place she could see her, and connect with her again. No-one else knew, no-one else could see. It was their time, their place.

Amanda knew it wouldn't be forever. She wouldn't always be able to come to the beach. Leyla wouldn't always be able to come to the beach.

But for now, that didn't matter. She was with her darling little girl once again, and, although her heart ached that she couldn't hold her, she could see she was well, and looked happy.

She watched as Leyla stood and picked up her bucket of treasure. She turned, looked at her mother and waved.

Amanda smiled at her daughter and waved back.

She watched as Leyla walked away then ran along the beach to join her father and grandparents, who she insisted bring her here almost every day since her mother had died.

Amanda could watch Leyla growing up. She knew these visits would become less and less. But while Leyla came to see her, she would be there, waiting.

~~~

Jaywick Sands

Tessa Thomson

When we heard he'd died we were by the sea
At Jaywick Sands, my mate and me.
Holidays I never got unless I went with Chrissie's lot.

Their clan was large, five kids and more,
But welcomed strays were catered for.
Food was found, beds made up,
    drinks to drink and food to sup.

Her mother read the news to us;
Our hearts broke and tears welled up.
Our Buddy's gone, our one true love;
    gone by plane to heaven above.

That'll Be the Day, we sang with all our hearts.
His soul and ours would never be apart.
Peggy Sue has got him now;
    his future songs are off the charts.

Other singers came and went
But none could match what Buddy meant
To two young girls at Jaywick Sands,
    lost in grief till summer's spent.

Jack

Wendy Fletcher

I stopped to take a photo and noticed you lying right next to my feet. You grinned up at me, as if to say, 'Nearly trod on me but, hey, I'm okay.'

Hooded lids sheltered your eyes from the glaring sun. You were dark against the pale sand. Something in that primate grin made you irresistible. I knew you would be heavy to carry, but I was drawn to pick you up.

I felt your weight against my chest as I brushed the sand from your smooth, rounded body.

I imagined how you would make my children laugh. I pictured you on my window ledge, or perhaps in the garden, greeting visitors with that infectious grin, from among the plants.

I walked on.

In the distance, a tree caught my eye, then another and another. They had tumbled from the cliff edge above, their roots outstretched, like grasping fingers, to cling to the soil for one last moment. Now they were a ragged forest sprawled on the shoreline, lying helpless, lapped by the waves.

I placed you by my bag and adjusted my camera to catch the light glowing on the pale wood.

Then I picked up my bag and turned to retrace my steps. In that moment, I saw baby terns. Fully-fledged now, they had escaped beneath the fencing that protected their nests. Waddling and wobbling down to the surf, wings slightly raised to balance their awkward gait, they called to each other excitedly and skidded to a halt as water foamed over their tiny feet and spindle legs.

I watched, mesmerised by this new life, as they took their first tentative steps into the froth. Another photo to frame a moment in time.

On again, to the point where the cliffs dipped and erosion had left them not much higher than the beach. It was just a step up, to be off the sand, following a winding path through vegetation that was safe from the encroaching sea, for now.

I was home before I missed you. Even then, I emptied the bag, believing I had popped you inside, although the weight belied this. Were you playing games with me? Would I see that cheeky grin as I neared the bottom?

You were not there. I looked out of the kitchen window at the darkening sky, and knew I had left you behind, to the incoming tide. I could see those wet fingers of foam crawling up the beach, seizing you, carrying you in a tumbling cascade as the water swept back.

I felt a sadness, a loss. We had met so briefly. My children would have loved you and introduced you to their friends. I wondered what they would have called you – Sea Monkey perhaps, or just Jack. Children are so unpredictable.

I did tell them about you at tea, but they didn't seem impressed. I couldn't convey to them the way you had looked up at me with that grin that made my face muscles twitch into an involuntary response so that I was grinning back.

I tried again at supper but by now the older ones had taken on that familiar 'Let's just humour her' expression.

'Perhaps someone else has found him.' My most sympathetic offspring offered. For a moment, I believed this. Despite the remoteness and the lateness of the day, it was possible. I visualised a small girl, clasping her mother's hand tightly, squealing, 'Oh, Mummy, look what I found,' then eagerly taking you home to meet her brothers. Perhaps you would find a home on her window ledge.

Then I saw the image of a petulant teenager, discarding you carelessly in a few years' time, and I realised that you didn't belong with her, or with me. You were already where you really belonged, tossing around in the sea of your life.

You had been formed at the edge of that sea, shaped and moulded by its pummelling.

For many years you must have come and gone with the tide, maybe sharing an odd moment in human company, enjoying the fact that you could make people laugh because nature had been kind to you, the centuries of currents carving you that face full of humour.

As I went to bed that night, I smiled to myself, knowing I had done the right thing, although that had not been my intention. What is on the beach, belongs on the beach and, if I chance upon you another day, on another walk, I will greet you cheerily, glad to see that you are visiting again, but I will resist your charm, wish you well and leave you to live your nomadic life with nature.

~~~

Roome Bay

Cathy Cade

Digger scampered onto the beach steps and turned to see if we were following. It was a pleasant morning. The wind had dropped overnight, and I was in no hurry. My husband would be packing away the motorhome's bed while the dogs were out of the way.

I paused at the top of the beach steps and gripped the rail, breathing the shellfishy, seaweedy air. Reassured, the white terrier carried on down the steps, her feathered tail waving from side to side. Pickle, the old brown Staffie, lumbered down a step at a time, her tail stiffly aloft.

On the sand, the dogs ran together, like children glad to be back on a beach. Then Digger sprang ahead to pounce after things that scuttled while Pickle and I ambled in the warmth. This little bay filled at high tide so its sand was still damp; unlikely to find its way into the skimpy pumps I'd forgotten to change.

On our previous visits here, I'd often continue along the beach at low tide and creep up on the campsite from below; it was a shorter route than returning over the crag. Getting to the campsite from the beach wasn't so much a climb as a clamber – like giant steps in the rock.

Pickle and I paused beside the middle flight of beach steps, where there was a ledge I could sit on. Once, Pickle would have leapt up beside me, but now she settled at my feet, glad of a rest. We watched clouds scudding across the seascape and listened to the rhythm of the waves.

Digger skipped across stones towards the sea, pausing to investigate a chunk of driftwood or paddle through a pool left by the tide. On her way back, she stopped to roll in a pile of seaweed. I hoped it wasn't too smelly; options for bathing her were limited in a motorhome.

Both terriers liked to roll in smelly patches, but these days Digger got there first and Pickle would walk past, not deigning to appear interested.

Pickle had taken on a new lease of life when the younger dog arrived nearly three years ago, although, at eleven, arthritis was already slowing her down. Unlike my husband, she wouldn't have the option of hip replacements. How could one explain to a dog that it mustn't twist its new hip?

I remembered how she used to corner at speed when chasing a rabbit, while the other dogs skidded like cartoon hounds. Digger seemed lively now, but she would collapse after our walk. She had neither the energy nor the staying power of Pickle in the days when she would barrel through undergrowth like a small brown tank. We had once seen her leap from a sitting start on the ground through the open driver's window of a Transit van.

I emptied sand from my shoe – it had sneaked in after all. I recalled distant holidays on sandy beaches with the children and Pickle's predecessors. Beaches were sunnier then.

Sand got into everything – food, clothes, towels, hair, fur.... It worked itself into car carpets and upholstery, lurking in crannies as the vacuum passed over it. The children would welcome it as we unpacked – a souvenir of their holiday.

Maybe aversion to sand is something that develops with age, like arthritis.

I stood to continue our walk, Pickle at my heels. Passing the final flight of steps, I headed for my campsite shortcut Digger ran ahead, skipping lightly over the stones at this end of the bay.

I chose my steps carefully across the first stony stretch, until I could relax onto the last flat patch of sand. Tomorrow I must come in trainers.

Like me, Pickle trod carefully over the stones. Where she had stepped out confidently two years ago, she now stumbled, her tail stiff and quivering.

Her legs were thicker than Digger's twiggy spindles, but they looked suddenly fragile.

Breakable.

Calling the dogs, I retraced our route across the sand to the steps. Watching Pickle cross the stones, I almost turned a heel myself. Digger was first up the steps to the promenade and already tearing around the grassy slope with a passing spaniel when Pickle and I took the circuitous footpath to join her.

Recognising the home stretch, the old dog picked up speed: trotting jauntily ahead with her companion jogging alongside. My husband would spot us returning over the cliff path and have the kettle on.

Later, on his new hips, he'd walk into Crail with us. He'd struggled with that walk on our last visit: determined – like Pickle – to master the pain.

There's life in us old dogs yet. Only a different life, at a different pace.

~~~

The Beach

Jan Cunningham

The little girl suddenly turned and realised the sea was rushing up to her at an alarming rate. The small bay was being rapidly closed off, water dashing over the rocks she had wandered round. She was frightened. Where was Mummy? The tears began to fall.

Then a voice said, "Do you need help, little one?"

She looked up and saw a young girl standing there. "Can you?"

"Oh yes," said the girl and promptly picked her up, straddled her on her hips and waded through the water, round the rocks, back to the larger beach.

She saw her Mummy waving frantically and with a quick thank-you she turned and ran as fast as she could into her mother's waiting arms.

Retired at last. Naomi was looking forward to doing all the things she hadn't had time for during her busy working life. She had always secretly wanted to explore the paranormal and last night had attended a psychic meeting at the local spiritual church for the first time.

During the coffee break, she discovered that a psychic weekend was being held at a nearby hotel in a fortnight's time. It was for everyone: beginners to fully-fledged psychics. She badly wanted to go but was apprehensive about going alone. Nothing ventured, nothing gained, she decided. They're only people after all. What could go wrong? In any case, she could always come home.

With some trepidation, Naomi checked into the hotel and took her case up to her room. When she returned to the lobby, people were sitting and chatting, with pre-dinner drinks. She looked around, feeling lost and out of place.

A voice behind her asked, "Are you new?"

Naomi turned to see a woman about her own age, smiling at her. She invited Naomi to sit and have a drink with her. She was so pleasant and easy to talk to, Naomi soon felt at ease, laughing at her anecdotes and telling a few of her own.

That was the start of a fascinating weekend. Naomi was in the beginners' group and took part in a variety of workshops. She most enjoyed the guided meditation sessions, with Annie, their group leader, who had a beautiful, low-pitched, warm, quiet voice and spoke slowly enough for Naomi to follow her instructions.

The last session for the beginners group was guided meditation, after which they would have a cup of tea together before making their way home.

Naomi entered the session and sat on one of the chairs. Music was playing softly in the background and Annie stood at the front waiting for the group to settle.

"Close your eyes, now, and listen to my voice. Imagine you are walking along a cliff top. The sun is hot and there are wispy clouds in the sky. The grass under your bare feet feels springy and coarse. You look down to the beach below. It is empty and inviting.

"You walk down steps to the beach and along the sand until you notice a beach towel laid out with a ripe peach sitting on it. You flop down on the towel, pick up the peach and sink your teeth into its plump, soft flesh. It is so refreshingly delicious you barely notice the juice running down your fingers and then your arms. When it is finished, you go into the sea to wash off the stickiness from the fruit. Then you turn to go back but you notice someone sitting by your towel. Who is it?"

Naomi involuntarily gasped out loud when she saw who was sitting by her towel. It was the young girl who had rescued her on the beach when she was a child.

Annie's voice was barely a whisper as she said, "Say hello to your Guardian Angel."

~~~

Atlantic Rollers

Wendy Fletcher

Atlantic Rollers
Crashing in,
What do you bring?
Pebbles and shingle
Shells galore,
Sea glass and more

Nanna's eyes smile,
She recalls the day
In Pembroke Bay
I was young
My hair was wild
Nanna's favourite child

What did the Rollers
Bring today?
I hear her say
Did you find treasure
On the sand?
I hold her wrinkled hand

Turning my head
I match her smile
Walk again that mile
Of golden beach
Bathed in sun
And we are one

Shifting sand
Between our toes
Better she never knows
Of the plastic
On the shore
Wildlife that is no more

A birthday balloon
With dragging tail
Torn cloth of a sail,
The bags and bottles
Choking her sea
I let her memories be

Balls of engine oil
Jagged edge of a can
The legacy of modern man
I can't tell her
What you bring,
Atlantic Rollers,
Crashing in

~~~

...

BITS AND PIECES

Flash, micro-fiction and verse

...

Wish You Were Here

Valerie Fish

Dear Mum and Dad,

Everybody here has been very kind to me.

It was a little girl.

I did what you asked.

I won't be coming back home,

Your loving daughter x

~~~

Caroline Cowan

Hi Mum,

Having a great time.

I'm still accident-prone. Went down the water flume, bikini top flew off. Camera at the bottom flashed, taking photo. Daren't go and collect it.

Went down rapids head-first. Head ended up against a large gentleman's backside. (Kiss-my-arse came to mind).

Decided to go feet first. No control over body going down; foot accidentally collided with same man's "unmentionables." Very painful!

Trying to be more vigilant.

Wish you were here.

Love, Cas.x

~~~

Wendy Fletcher

Dear Mum,

I am so frightened. I wish you were here to hold my hand. I am confined in this narrow space, and it is so dark. Close on either side I can just see brick walls. They are wet and I feel so cold. Above me, more bricks form an arch and water drips from them. My hair is getting wet and I am shivering.

Below me, dark water swirls and I do not know its depth. Behind me, is only darkness and ahead I can see a single light. It is coming toward me....

Just to reassure you, we passed the other narrow boat without mishap and are now safely out of the Blisworth tunnel. By the time I post this, we will have reached Stoke Bruerne and I will have had a hot shower on board.

Enjoying my canal holiday, Wendy.

~~~

Valerie Fish

Dear Mum and Dad

Surprise! Angela and I were married yesterday.

I know this must be a huge shock for you both, but please try to understand. She is my best friend, my rock, the love of my life. Be happy for us.

Sorry Dad, you didn't get to walk me down the aisle. Your loving daughter, Susan. Xx

~~~

Cathy Cade

Hi Mum!

You know I never meant to run your Mercedes into that tree, but I'm *so* pleased they paid out on the insurance so I could come here.

I miss your cooking. Food here is weird. They make us exercise every day to 'maintain muscle tone' – but exercise is a doddle when I feel so much lighter.

Shane tried to kid me you were letting my room while I'm away, LOL. Sorry if I've been a pain the last year or so. We talk about home a lot in here – although I think some people over-react sometimes.

The journey here was a drag; I'm not looking forward to the trip back. Blast-off is meant to be the worst bit though, isn't it? So I'm sure touchdown will be fine too – you mustn't worry about it.

Anyhow, that's weeks and weeks away.

Thanks again for bankrolling my trip on the SpaceLine.

Love, Kayleigh

~~~

Val Chapman

Oliver

This is a very hard thing to write, but I have to tell you that my dear Sam has sadly died. I know that you saw him a lot and got close to him before you went to University, so I felt you should know.

I can tell you that it was sudden, and it may be of comfort to know that he did not suffer. In fact, he had been out for a run that very morning, and had met up with some friends in the park.

It was just as he arrived back home that he collapsed and died within a few minutes so, as you would expect, the family are all in a state of shock.

I know it's early days, but in time we may find ourselves with another dog though, of course, it would never replace Sam, the best Border Collie in the world.

Mavis

~~~

Wendy Fletcher

Hi Mum,

Can't believe I've been here a week already. Time going quickly. The food's good. Most of the staff speak quite good English.

Write soon.

Sam Smith

HMP Glasgow

~~~

Jan Cunningham

Hi Ma, Pa.

Having a fab time. Sea, sun and sangria, what more could a girl want?

Mum you once said to me, "Don't come home with more than you went." Which I didn't... until now. I'm so sorry.

But I couldn't tell you before I left 'cos I didn't know myself. To say it was a surprise to me is an understatement, but it can't be helped.

I have to stay a little bit longer as we can't fly yet due to some regulations or other. Still hope to be home in time for your birthday, Mum, when I will bring my little extra to visit you. I know you and Dad will love it as much as I do when you meet.

Oh, by the way, it's house-trained and everything.

Love you lots and lots M

P.S. Will send some piccies as soon as poss. Xx

~~~

Val Chapman

Mum,

Just to let you know that everything is great. The place is lovely, and the people are really nice – friendly, helpful, and kind. Honestly, considering it is the first time I have been abroad on my own, I am taking it all in my stride and loving it.

The next couple of weeks are going to be amazing. I have already booked a boat trip to a little bay, where hopefully, we can swim with dolphins. Obviously, I will be careful though, and I am only going to be doing the activities for the first week, because I'll be resting up for the second.

I still find it amazing how much money I saved by coming here instead of staying at home. I am happy and excited, and looking forward to the operation.

So I will see you in a couple of weeks, with my new boobs!

Love, Rachel.

~~~

Cathy Cade

Dear Peter,

I hope Bouncer's behaving and you're not overfeeding him. Don't let him sleep on your furniture.

Malta's hotter than I remember. I mentioned I was stationed here in the '70s and the hotel owner – who can't have been long out of nappies at the time – has taken to regaling your mum with scurrilous 'British soldier' anecdotes in the bar. I go up to bed and leave them to it.

We got chatting with a receptionist here, Petra, who told us her mother died recently. When your mum went off souvenir shopping, Petra was off duty so I bought her a drink and one thing led to another. We discovered we had more in common than we'd realised.

I must say, your mum's been very understanding.

She'll be coming home as scheduled and will collect Bouncer.

I'll stay here until Petra can get away. She's looking forward to meeting her half-brother – Dad

~~~

Flashes of Inspiration

Result
Teresa Gilbertson

It had been surprisingly easy to dispose of her husband. Nobody had even suspected her.

Maybe she shouldn't have done it, but she couldn't take any more of his violent behaviour. With just one discreet push, he fell to his fate, his last words echoing in her ears.

'That's the way to do it.'

Then Punch became lunch as Mr. Crocodile hungrily swallowed him up.

~~~

Choc
Tessa Thomson

Cadburys chocolate expectation,
Silver wrapping scintillation,
Cubes of heaven anticipation,
In the mouth, glorification
On the hips, mortification,
Promises of rectification.
No more chocolate expectation.

~~~

Pea-brained
Valerie Fish

I've a brain the size of a pea;
Learning never came easy for me,
But I've a heart of gold
Which is worth, so I'm told,
Far more than a fancy degree

~~~

Early Days
Val Chapman

He hid in the shadows, pushing his back hard into the wall to avoid being noticed.

He needed to settle after his initial exuberance and take stock of his surroundings. He had explored the area, getting his bearings, and now tried to calm himself until he felt brave enough to venture further.

He heard a sound to his left, and turned his head to check out the noise.

"Izzy, leave him alone. He's just a puppy. He'll come out to you in his own time."

~~~

The Beast
Wendy Fletcher

I held my breath as the beast drew closer. I could hear its lumbering, rumbling approach and I knew this was my last chance to run, but my feet were rooted in the grass.

I had hesitated a moment too long and now its eyes were upon me, yellow and blurry in the early morning mist.

It towered over me, stopping suddenly and opening its cavernous mouth. I felt its hot breath as it swallowed me into its dark body and the mouth closed.

There was no escape now. I was already being carried away by the dreaded school bus.

~~~

Tangible Assets
Valerie Fish

Her brain was the size of a pea
Her cup size a huge Double D
She wasn't that dumb,
Success was to come
Flaunting her assets on page three.

~~~

O
Stephen Oliver

O is.

But how can there be existence when there is no time? No past. No present. No future.

And if there is no time, there can be no space. No place. No motion.

And if there is neither time nor space, how can O exist?

And yet... O is.

O is the potential, the possibility, the maybe, the perhaps.

There is nothing.

Just O.

There is everything.

Time, space, energy, matter, actuality. It is all here, reaching to the edges of infinity for eternity.

O is the universe, all that was and is and can be.

O is...

Us.

~~~

Hedgehogs
Phil Cumberland

"Do you like hedgehogs?" I asked.

"Yes," said Fred, "but I couldn't eat a whole one."

"It's all you think about, your stomach."

"Well, there is a lot of it to think about."

"I didn't mean edibility, or lack of it, but hedgehogs in more general terms."

"In general terms, yes I like them but road safety and traffic awareness isn't something they excel at, is it?"

"What do you suggest – a sort of Tufty club for hedgehogs? Spikey's, perhaps – a learned old Hedgehog with a blackboard and easel teaching the finer points of zebra crossings instead of the roll-up-in-a-ball method?"

"I could just perhaps manage half of one, on second thoughts."

~~~

SMS
Cathy Cade

Getting the. Hang of txting on new fone. Mum said 2 get. My head out of it or she d take it away so i cum out 2 buy comic from shop over the. Road   if she thinks she ca

17.14

~~~

Thin Ice
Caroline Cowan

Rob, knew the danger sign was there, but ignored it.

The ice was wafer thin, but he was bullying Rick, the youngest of his gang to walk on it. Rick didn't want to be called a coward.

The first steps seemed OK. He turned and waved.

The cracking sound was loud. Rick suddenly disappeared into the dark depths of the freezing water. The gang looked on in horror.

Rob, now a quiet family man, stared at the photo of the small boy, and brushed away a silent tear. Oh, how he wished he could turn back the clock.

~~~

Inspired
Valerie Fish

She never bothered telling him where she was going, and he never bothered asking. He wouldn't have cared anyway. He was constantly putting her down, making her feel worthless.

It was all so different on a Thursday morning. She felt valued; people actually listened to what she had to say.

She was thrilled when it was suggested her latest work was good enough to be published.

Maybe now was the time to tell her husband what she had been up to; after all he had been the inspiration for her story, 'How to commit the perfect murder.'

~~~

Over the Hill
Cathy Cade

I could exercise more, truth to tell;
Join the walking group with my dog, Belle,
If the old girl could still tackle six miles – with hills...
The dog's got arthritis as well.

~~~

U3A Agents
Caroline Cowan

The usher at the cinema door stepped back in awe of the U3A Agents. They flashed their badges with pride.

Being screened was a cowboy film, with plenty of shooting. As the lights came up at the end, a man lay slumped over the seat, shot.

"Stay calm," shouted Jo. "Everything is under control. We are the U3A Agents and will deal with the situation."

With that statement a man gasped with horror and instantly dropping his gun, pleaded guilty.

"That was quickly solved," they chorused. "The U3A have won the Murder Mystery Day."

~~~

Atonement
Valerie Fish

Tired of living a life of vice
She went to her priest for advice
'You must renounce your sin
But before you begin
One last performance would be nice'

~~~

The One Left Behind
Tessa Thomson

He woke early as they had always done, anxious to start their day together.

But now the days stretched out in front of him like dark clouds over a grey sea. Sadness that he thought he could never survive was his constant companion.

People came and went but no one came for him.

She came; she was for him.

She would touch his hand, brush his forehead, kiss his lips. Inside he knew the words to say, but no voice of his could be heard. His silent world kept them apart.

Now she was gone before him, and he was invisible, but screaming inside.

~~~

Rejection Dejection
Cathy Cade

When submitting to contests and 'zines
I pore over all of my scenes
Dot my i's, cross each t,
Tick each box that I see,
But push all the wrong buttons, it seems

~~~

Anthem for the U3A
Jan Cunningham

Merrily we roll along,
roll along, roll along,
Merrily we roll along to the U3A.

Cycle, walk or play ping pong,
play pingpong, play pingpong,
Fitness is for everyone, in the U3A.

Learn to talk in foreign tongues,
foreign tongues, foreign tongues,
Honi soi qui mal y pense, at the U3A.

Garden, craft or sing a song,
sing a song, sing a song,
Come and try you can't go wrong in the U3A.

We live and learn and laugh a lot,
laugh a lot, laugh a lot.
Some think we have lost the plot at the U3A.

But we don't care, we'll carry on,
having fun, having fun,
Till the setting of our sun – in the U3A.

~~~

...

BEGIN AT THE END

A slip of paper passed three times to add a word.
Then passed again.

Given words are **emphasised** in the final paragraph.

The Old Samurai

Tessa Thomson

An old and lonely Samurai
was sitting by the bay,
His head held in his hands,
his thoughts a way away.
His sword lay by his side.
His costume lay there too,
But hands once firm were shaking.
He knew not what to do.

His sword, once light inside those hands
felt heavy now to lift.
He knew disaster lay ahead;
those thoughts were hard to shift.
He thought again about the gun,
the young man's tool of choice,
But could he break tradition?
And then he heard his father's voice.

"Stand up my Son and be a man.
"Take up your sword again.
"Put on your clothes, prepare to act.
"Tradition must remain."

The audience is waiting.
The players stand in line.
Once more he heads towards the stage,
a man on borrowed time.
The gun would be the easy way,
the sword would be his past,
His father's way to beat the shame,
a Samurai to the last.

But not today, the old man thought.
I'll see another dawn.
I'll raise my sword in honour.
My duty I have sworn.
Tradition lingers with the old
and dies with old ones too.
Younger men can live with shame
and give it its fair due.

An old and lonely **Samurai**
still sitting by the bay,
Deciding how to live
what may be his longest day.
How best to end **disaster**
and hide the shame and pain,
To lift the sword or raise the **gun**.

Tradition wins again.

~~~

Best Intentions

Teresa Gilbertson

Wandering aimlessly along rough tracks surrounded by woodland, he wondered how it could all have gone so wrong.

It had been in all the nationals and huge TV debates had followed. He had purchased the ancient woodland in order to improve access to the village, thereby encouraging much-needed tourism. Having the oldest, most attractive village in England was no asset if it remained practically inaccessible. The locals had been fully supportive of his plans when first approached.

Then the press became involved. Environmentalists demonstrated, marching on Downing Street and rallying in Hyde Park. How was he to know public opinion was so strong? They were only a few old trees, no good for anything, and felling them would bring wealth to the village.

Well, he had certainly put the village on the map now. Never had it received so much attention – and from such high places, too. Its seclusion and inaccessibility had become the focal points for the location of the next high security prison site.

He had to lie low until public outrage had subsided. He could not go **home**; he must move on. If the villagers **caught** him, he would be dead. Strange, that the very thing that led to the outcry should now offer him shelter amongst its wooded depths. But all was not **lost**. The village would still have the wealth it had craved, albeit from different visitors.

~~~

The Exam

Wendy Fletcher

The memory of sitting the exam has already blurred in my mind, although it was just a few short weeks ago.

If I screw up my eyes tight, I can picture the room, small and square. I'm not sure if I am imagining it on that particular day or any other day when it was just a classroom.

Was it any different?

Yes, I recall sunlight. That was different. Perhaps it was the only time I saw it with the blinds open.

We usually spent an hour or two each week in that dark space, focussed on the black and white television set that was a recent addition to school property.

We watched Programmes for Schools on the BBC.

I remember the characters in costume from Anglo-Saxon times and the maps that moved to show a close-up of the areas of Europe where these people had started their voyages.

On those occasions there had been a large group of us, squashed into a small seating area, although large is a relative term. In this instance, it had been about seven, only large because it was the entire top year.

I hear sounds now: our chatter as we filed in, and again as we filed out. Only on exam day was the room

Silent; a silence that spread out into the short corridor and extended into a hush that enveloped the whole building.

No talking allowed. No exchange of ideas beforehand. No comparisons afterwards.

The image of a stranger emerges from the corner of the room and I feel again the sense of occasion that his presence brought to us. We were not in the care of the two teachers who have nurtured us from the age of five. That day we were handed over to the stranger with an even stranger name. I think it was in-vig-il-a-tor or something similar.

He was there not to care for us but to 'supervise'. It was a taste of things to come. Whichever way this exam went, it would lead us to a world of strangers.

We would be leaving this familiar building where we had been safely cocooned for the last seven years, just seventy of us, all living within a mile of the gate.

Some of us would be heading for the big school in the nearby town and some of us might be catching a bus to travel twelve miles across the Fens to the Grammar School in another town that most of us had never even visited.

I can't remember if it was a cold morning or warm. I don't recall a cardigan so it might have been mild, and I don't think it rained.

I do have recollections of writing in pencil and the reassurance of seeing each place set with a rubber. In

class, we are now beginning to write in pen:
sophisticated young people with the confidence to
commit our thoughts straight to paper without
hesitation or the chance to change our minds. But, on
exam day, it was back to the security of knowing that
we could take a chance and still retract our thoughts if
we were not satisfied with the result, or if a better idea
came to mind half-way down the page.

I can't remember what the questions said.

Were they easy? Were they hard? Did I understand
them? Did I even read them?

Could it be that they are not familiar because I just
sat there in a silent panic and read nothing?

Might I have written nothing?

Was my paper collected by the in-vig-il-a-tor man as
white and unmarked as when it was placed in front of
me?

From the depths of my subconscious rises another
image. It's a lion on a bus. I squint against the unlikely
scene but it is definitely a lion and it's definitely on the
upper deck of a red double-decker. Gradually the story
unfolds. It has escaped from the local zoo. It has
casually sauntered along the High Street on a quiet
Sunday morning and caught the Number 19 when it
pulled up to drop a passenger.

The driver, safely enclosed in his cab, drives on
unaware and it is the heroic conductress who has to
calmly save all the passengers.

As the story plays back to me, it is all familiar. I recognise the characters because I created them. I recognise the words because they are mine.

I feel reassured. Those are the words I captured on the exam paper. It was not blank when I handed it in, or at least the Composition section was not, I'm still not sure about the arithmetic bit or the grammar questions.

Perhaps more will come back to me later as I try again to settle for the night. I have been to bed but got up again, first for the toilet, then for a drink. Now I look for an extra pillow so that I can prop myself up and see if the unopened book will take my mind off my troubled thoughts.

I know I will not sleep tonight. My mind is full of strange faces and strange places and the haunting image of catching that bus across the Fens.

I know I will not sleep tonight because **tomorrow** the post will bring that slip of **paper**, the passport for me to **climb** towards whatever new goals lie ahead of me.

~~~

Changing Fortune

Valerie Chapman

Gabrielle turned and looked at Oaklands Manor for what she guessed would be the last time.

Due to 'personal circumstances' her beautiful home had been sold, and Gabrielle was off to pastures new.

Personal circumstances? Well, I suppose that covers it, she thought.

She was partly to blame; she knew that. She had tried to save it, but to no avail.

In marrying Nicholas, a professional gambler, it was always at risk.

Ha, how ironic. Gabrielle had never bet on anything, and yet her entire existence had been used as a stake in a game of cards.

Her father had warned her time and time again, but she had ignored him, choosing to believe that things would be fine. She and Nicholas would stand together and work together. After all, he had always come up trumps – pardon the pun – and during the leaner times, her father's successful packaging business helped them out.

She had wanted to be more involved in the business, but she had no aptitude for it, and felt out of her depth whenever she tried to get to grips with the whole thing.

Her father, bless him, had tried to get his son-in-law involved in the business too, but Nicholas couldn't, or wouldn't entertain the idea. Being a businessman wasn't his 'style'; he preferred the excitement of the poker tables and roulette wheel.

The family had discussed what to do with the business on her father's retirement – or worse. After all, there was no point in Gabrielle taking it on, though as an only child, that might have been expected. She, or Nicholas, would bankrupt it within months.

Before a decision could be reached however, Gabrielle's parents were killed in a car crash. The business, and the beautiful Oaklands Manor, were now the responsibility of Gabrielle and Nicholas.

She did try, really she did, but Nicholas saw it, and her, as a 'cash cow'. That, combined with a few dodgy business decisions, had brought them to where they were now, with Nicholas serving time in prison for fraud, among other things, leaving Gabrielle with almost nothing.

Forced to sell both the business and the Manor House to cover debts, she had managed to keep enough to buy a tiny cottage in a nearby village but once the money ran out... what then?

A little job, she supposed. But what could she do?

She had always relied on the men in her life to provide everything she wanted.

What an idiot, she now realised.

Ah well, Gabrielle thought. Maybe it was time to find out what she was made of.

~

Thirty years later

She'd had time, lately, to reflect.

Losing her home, her livelihood, her money, could have been the making of Gabrielle, forcing her to face up to her situation and triumph over adversity. In reality, though, she hadn't risen to the challenge and had led a very mundane, uninspiring and unhappy life.

She had managed to find a succession of little jobs in the village coffee shop, the newsagent, and one of the local takeaways. Earning just enough to pay her way, she faced retirement with no private pension to fall back on.

She hadn't remarried. Nicholas had died of cancer many years ago, just after leaving prison, and there was no family to speak of on either side.

Gabrielle too was in poor health and struggled to look after herself and her home. With no-one to help, she felt she had no choice but to give up her cottage, and live in a retirement home. At least leaving here wouldn't be as hard as leaving Oaklands had been.

There hadn't been a huge selection of places for Gabrielle to choose from, so someone from social services had told her where she would be going. She didn't care. The way she was feeling, she doubted she would be there long.

She was being collected today to go to her new home.

Well, her new room anyway.

She sat in her old green armchair, surrounded by a few cardboard boxes containing all her worldly goods.

It wasn't a long journey, and the chatty young lady who accompanied her was very nice. She assured Gabrielle that this home had had a complete refurbishment and was thought to be one of the nicest places around, considering.

As they drove into the car park, Gabrielle gave a wry **smile**. Despite the name change, Oaklands **Manor House** still looked more or less the same since the renovations. It would be interesting living in one of the new rooms which had once been the old **stable-block**. After all these years, she'd never expected to be living back here again.

~~~

Mum's Surprise

Jan Cunningham

"No! I don't believe it! Oh, my God what am I going to do? Not now, please not now!" came the panicky voice of his wife from the utility room.

"What's up, love?" called Joe from the kitchen.

"The bloody freezer's broken down and everything has defrosted," she replied.

Joe knew the freezer was packed to the gunnels with food – party stuff for her mother's seventieth birthday next weekend. And how she had crowed about it, because Iceland (which all mothers go to) had lots of offers on party food and she had filled her boots, or rather the freezer, with every conceivable goody they had.

"What the hell am I going to do? I spent a fortune and I can't afford to just go out and buy another freezer and fill it again. Anyway, the offers will have finished by now. Oh, Joe, why me? Why now?"

"Problems?" asked Milly, their youngest daughter, wandering into the kitchen.

"The freezer's broken down," said Joe.

"All the food your mum bought for Nana's birthday bash has defrosted so we'll have to chuck it. Your mum's raging."

"OMG! Like, wow! No wonder Mum's mad. I helped her carry it all back from the shop and the bags weighed a ton. What are we going to do?"

"Haven't a clue," replied Joe, "but we better come up with something quick or Mum will explode."

Sue came into the kitchen, sat down at the table, put her head in her hands and cried.

"I've bought and planned everything for Mum's 70th," she wailed. "She thinks we're taking her out, but I've managed to get all the family and her friends to come here and that's no mean feat I can tell you. Now it's ruined. I'll have to ring everyone and tell them it's off."

"Wait a minute," said Milly. "I've just had a brill idea. Why don't we have the party this weekend – tomorrow in fact. Then we could use up all the food. It will be okay till tomorrow if we decant it into the fridge and then cook it all up won't it?"

"Don't be daft," replied Sue. "Our fridge can't hold all that food, and people will have already made arrangements for this weekend."

"Don't be so defeatist, Mum. Okay, then what about having a street party? Like we had a few years ago for some royal something or other. It was great. We all had a whale of a time."

"You do have some mad ideas." Joe laughed. "But hey, why not? Let's at least give it a go. Milly, you go round the neighbours and invite them for coffee at eleven a.m. Tell them it's an emergency and we need help. I'll phone your Nana first to see if she's free to come over and if it's a yes, I'll start phoning the rest of the family and Nana's friends to see how many of them can make it. What do you say Sue? Shall we at least give it a go?"

Sue, with tears still running down her cheeks, just shrugged. Joe and Milly disappeared to make a start on the rescue mission.

Joe phoned Ada first, Sue's Mum, to see if she was free tomorrow and how about her coming over for her tea? She said she was, and she'd love to.

Prompt at eleven, the neighbours arrived, and as Joe served the coffee he explained their predicament.

"It was Milly's idea to throw a street party to use up the food and have Ada's 'do' a week early. She thinks she's just coming for her tea. How about it?" asked Joe. "I know it's short notice but we are desperate."

"Let's take a vote," said their next-door neighbour, Mick. "Hands up those willing to help. Personally, I think it will be a hoot. Weather forecast is sound and a street get-together sounds fun. Me and Anne will help out; we've nothing special on and the kids will love it. Maybe hook up some music... What do you think?"

The family's luck was in and most of the neighbours were willing and able. They divvied up the contents of the freezer, and each took what they could.

"What about the minced beef and joints of lamb?" Sue groaned. "They won't keep. I'll have to chuck them, and there was quite a bit too cos I buy them when they're on offer."

"Give them to me," said Cathy, another neighbour. "I'll make the mince into chilli that we can serve with French bread. The joints, I'll slow-roast and then 'pull' the meat to use in rolls." Cathy's cooking skills were legendary.

Joe then set about ringing everyone on the list Sue gave him of those who had been invited, explaining why the change of plan and asking if they could make this Saturday instead.

Saturday morning dawned bright and sunny. Soon front doors opened and all sorts of tables – formica, picnic, kitchen – were being carried out into the street. As the street was actually a Close there would be no through traffic to worry about. Someone had the good idea to borrow trestle tables from the local church and invite the vicar along as well.

All day long, the street was a hive of activity. Those that had leftover party decorations were happily stringing them up wherever they could. They were a mismatched trawl of Happy Birthdays from 3 to 65 but nobody cared, it just made things more festive. Fairy lights were dragged out of lofts and wrapped around trees in the gardens, and the tables were covered with an array of highly coloured cloths ranging from plastic to cotton to paper, all anchored by vases of flowers donated by some of the neighbours. Paper plates, dishes, cutlery and glasses were added last. The smell of food, being prepared in various kitchens all along the Close, drifted over the street and made everyone's mouth water.

By six o'clock the stage was set.

All it needed now was a show of friends and relatives to help make the party swing. As Joe got in his car to fetch Ada, the first guests were arriving. He sighed with relief and drove away.

Ada's face, when she saw the street full of friends and relatives, lit up first with shock and then with joy. But when Sue told it was her birthday party, she looked puzzled.

"My birthday isn't till next Saturday," she said. "You know that."

"I know, Mum, but..."

And Sue told her the sorry tale of the freezer and why they had thrown a street party and incorporated her birthday into it, so as not to waste all the food.

"Don't worry, Mum, we'll still have a bit of a 'do' next week. For those who couldn't make tonight, I'm doing afternoon tea and you can open your cards and pressies on the right day."

Ada didn't mind at all and threw herself into the party, which was already going with a swing. The Close was alive with the sound of music, chattering and laughter; the food was quickly demolished. Everyone agreed they had a great time.

Sunday morning, the phone rang, Sue answered it to hear her Mum squealing, "I've won, I've won!"

"Mum, Mum, slow down. What are you on about? What have you won at 11 o'clock on a Sunday morning?"

"The People's Lottery!" shouted Ada down the phone. "You know, the one you see on the tele. I thought I'd give it a go a few months back, just for a bit of fun, and now I've won a shed-load of money!"

Sue sat down heavily on a kitchen chair. "How much, Mum? Are you sure it's kosher? Not some scam or other?"

"No, love, it's all above board and I've won £30,000! I nearly **fell** over when the young man on my doorstep this morning pulled this enormous cheque out of a gold envelope. I never, in a million years, thought I would be so lucky. Well now I can help you. You know how **grateful** I've been for all your help since your Dad died. Now you can go and buy a new **chest** freezer and fill it up, courtesy of me and The People's Lottery!"

~~~

Where Does the Pope Buy His Frocks?

Philip Cumberland

"I often talk to myself, sometimes out loud, mostly though within the confines of my mind. I am not sure whether it is just my way of marshalling thoughts or a rehearsal of how the words may sound when spoken."

"That's very interesting, Mr Fontain," said Miss Rogers, my analyst, "But you must realise there are times when sharing your thoughts vocally may not be appropriate."

"I don't know, sometimes it can liven up a boring occasion, even make it interesting."

"It can cause offence though."

"No one has the right not to be offended."

"What about the occasion of the Queen's visit?"

"All I said was she is not my mum and I wish she would stop sending me begging letters."

"But why use the megaphone?"

"She was a long way off and I wanted her to hear. I am fed up with her writing to me. I don't even know the woman. It got a lot of laughs though, a cheer and a round of applause."

"What about the fight afterwards?"

"The Queen started that – well some of the blokes with her did."

"The police?"

"They had no right to try and steal my megaphone; it cost me a lot of money. It is a good job the people nearby thought the same. I've still got my megaphone thanks to them."

"Would those people be the Fens Republicans?"

"I think some of them might be. I know a couple come from Ely, some from Chatteris and at least one from Huntingdon."

"The Queen had to cut short her visit because of the fighting; a lot of people were very disappointed."

"Well they shouldn't have started the fights then should they? As I said, no one has the right not to be offended. When I am offended, I don't start fighting people and trying to steal their stuff, do I?"

"No, you use your megaphone. What about the visit by the Pope to Cambridge?"

"All I said was I wonder if he got his frock from Marks and Spencer or John Lewis."

"Through your megaphone, wasn't it?"

"Most people thought it was hilarious. I think even the Pope had a chuckle."

"That caused more trouble."

"The police again, trying to nick my megaphone. It was a good job most of the crowd were on my side, and I had my bike handy for a swift getaway."

"The getaway caused problems too, didn't it?"

"The students on their bikes, you mean?"

"Yes. They blocked off most of the roads in the city centre to stop the police, didn't they?"

"I heard about that. Again, it was the police causing trouble; you would think they would be chasing criminals wouldn't you?"

"How on earth did you manage to smuggle your megaphone into Parliament?"

"It wasn't easy. I had it wrapped up in a parcel and pretended to be a courier delivering it to an MP. Once I was in, I got changed and sneaked into the chamber."

"But why shout out 'Black Rod stole my elephant'?"

"Because what I really feel, what I **genuinely** believe, I cannot say. My **voice** is silent on the really important issues – on the lessons we haven't **learned**. Mostly, I talk to myself; that audience always listens."

"Okay, Mr Fontain, same time next week. Back to your cell now."

~~~

Three Little Words

Valerie Fish

Write a word on your piece of paper. Pass it on to the next person. Do this three times, and everybody ends up with three words, which have to be included in the last paragraph of your story.

'This sounds fun,' I thought. Wrong! I was not happy with the hand I'd been dealt. Two of my words didn't seem too bad and could possibly go together, but as for the third... how on earth was I going to fit that in with the others, and at the end of my story?

It had all been going so well. Last month's assignment had been right up my alley – done and dusted the very next day. This one was definitely not going to be an easy ride.

Back home, first thing I did was look up my pesky word in my online dictionary. Of course, I knew what it meant but had a daft notion that actually reading the official definition might give me inspiration. No chance. Good old Roget was no help either.

My next daft idea was to simply change it: swap it for something of my choice that would go nicely with the other two. Who would know?

Well I would know. And that would be cheating.

My mind was cast back fifty years to my grammar school days. My geography teacher had caught me copying my best friend's work (obvious because we both had the same wrong answer). I remember him saying, 'The only person you're cheating is yourself'. His words stuck with me; it was a lesson learnt.

So I kept my word, treating it as a challenge to be overcome, telling myself how pleased I would be when I completed the task. I'd go to bed at night with those three words whirling round in my head, waking up the next morning no nearer to an answer. This went on right up till the day before our next meeting.

I had my other U3A hat on; it was singing afternoon. A few of the girls were, like me, in both the creative writing and singing groups. They'd finished their assignments and posted them online – all very impressive. I was feeling disheartened and time was running out but, as usual, as soon as I started to sing my troubles were forgotten. Eureka! It hit me, why hadn't I thought of that before!

The following morning, I was literally singing my way to the meeting, a big smile on my face, thinking how daft I was to have been so **perplexed** about it all.

'**Dancing** in the **moonlight**, everybody's feeling warm and bright.'

~~~

Rough Justice

Cathy Cade

At the end of the drove, a white van turned off the road and its lights went out.

'Hello – what's he up to?'

But his wife was already asleep.

He had been checking the solar lights in the front garden before closing the curtains, to identify how many needed replacing. He'd buy them from the pound shop tomorrow – they lasted as long as the ones he'd bought last summer from the garden centre.

The moon was hidden tonight behind gathering storm clouds. Out here, surrounded by fields, there were no street lights. The solar lights in some of the front gardens illuminated nothing. He could just make out that the van had stopped before reaching their terraced cottages.

He heard nothing for a while, but his hearing wasn't what it used to be. Then the van doors closed quietly – but you can't close a car door properly without some sound. The engine must have been idling, because it didn't start up again before he heard tyres rolling past. Past the terraces, the van accelerated, and its lights came on at the far end of the drove.

In the morning, he pulled back the curtains to see a pile of rubbish at the edge of the field opposite. There was battered cardboard and black bags and what looked like an open fridge. Later, on their way out, they drove past slowly to get a better look. A battered teddy bear waved at them. Broken glass glinted against the growing sugar beet.

They had lunch while they were out and were gone some time. When they returned, someone had cleared away the rubbish.

'Quick, that rat's back under the bird feeder.'

At his nod, his wife slowly opened the kitchen window, careful not to disturb the feeding rat. He aimed his loaded rifle through the open window.

Snap!

The rat leapt into the air and dropped out of sight. He replaced the rifle and went out to find the body. It was amazing how far a dead rat could travel before it realised it was dead.

'You got 'im then,' she called as he inspected it.

'Straight through the head.'

'Let's hope that's the last of 'em.'

'Last of that nest, anyway.'

He took the rat by its tail and threw it in the dyke at the end of the garden. They saw no more rats that week.

Ten nights later, he was closing the bedroom curtains when he again saw the white van turning into the drove. Its lights went out.

The moon was bright that night and almost full. He watched two men get out and move to the back of the van. He couldn't see what they were unloading there, but he could guess.

'Them rats are back with more rubbish.'

This time she was awake. 'Can you see their number-plate?'

'Not from here; the light's turned off. I'll see if I can read it from the downstairs window.'

He was halfway down when her raised whisper reached him. 'Don't let them see you nosing. They might cause trouble if they see you're looking.'

The stairs creaked as she followed him down.

'Don't you go outside.'

She'd spent much of their married life trying to restrain what she saw as his recklessness. They'd met after he left the Service, and she never could appreciate the swift assessment that preceded his seemingly rash reactions.

The front door key resisted his attempt to turn it quietly, and by the time he got to the gate the van was rolling past the last cottage.

This time, the rubbish was there for two days before a truck came to clear it. He spoke with the council workers, but all he could tell them was the fly-tippers had come in a white van. No help at all.

Useless.

Every night now, he watched for a while from the bedroom window before he went to bed. He left the curtains and window open, to let the night sounds into their bedroom. A month went by, and then another.

It was the early hours of a muggy morning when the fly-tippers returned. He was woken by the crunch of tyres on the gravel now scattered across the drove and disturbed his wife as he was getting out of bed.

'What is it?'

But already he was at the stairs.

She appeared at the door of the front room as he was lifting his loaded rifle from its new place behind the corner cabinet.

'What... you can't–'

'Shh!'

He hoped her stage-whisper hadn't carried through the open window. He knew he must shoot before they got back in the van, but still, he must aim carefully.

The report merged with the sound of glass shattering. Moments later, the van doors slammed and the engine roared. Along the drove, windows creaked against wooden frames, and metal hinges squealed.

Voices protested.

The van sped past them all and away down the drove.

'They won't dump their rubbish here again. Not if it's going to cost them a new windscreen.'

'You could've hit one of them.'

He didn't deign to answer that.

'They'll know it was us. They'll come back.'

'Could've been anyone along here.'

'What if...'

But she'd run out of protests. They were hardly likely to report it to the police.

Upstairs, he stood again at the window and looked over dark fields. He heard his wife getting into bed behind him. Along the terrace, voices gradually stilled and windows closed.

He felt... operational.

Useful.

A fox's shriek **cried** a warning. He had moved to the **Fens** to avoid the kind of retribution he'd just courted. The sky began to lighten behind the black **trees** patrolling the horizon. He closed the window and went to bed smiling.

~~~

FRAGMENTS

Other prose and poetry from the group,
Some new, some previously published.

.

My Singapore

Valerie Fish

I first arrived on the island of Singapore in the arms of a handsome sailor, or so my mother tells me; I was only three years old at the time.

Apparently, Mum was struggling down the gangplank carrying me and holding on to the railings for dear life when, seeing her plight, a handsome sailor took me from her and deposited me safely on Malaysian soil.

It was June 1959, and my dad had been seconded to RAF Changi in his role of Meteorological Assistant. It had been a long trip: six weeks, with various stops along the way. We're not talking luxury cruise liners here; this was a cargo ship, and there were only about twenty civilian passengers.

So began an exciting three years for the Hitchings family.

Dad was officer status and entitled to officer's quarters at the RAF base. As Mum and Dad had made friends with another couple on the way over, they decided to live off-base, renting adjoining bungalows just around the corner from the famous Changi jail. The friendship continued when both families returned home, and I have many happy memories of going to stay with them in Wiltshire.

Singapore offered a life of luxury for my mother. She had a live-in amah, (nanny, housemaid and cook rolled into one) so Mum didn't have to do any cooking or housework. On the amah's day off we went out to eat. Mum's excuse was that it was too hot for her to cook. She did have a point, with temperatures in the thirties all year round. We also had a kabun (gardener).

Life for the RAF families was one big social whirl of whist drives, coffee mornings and cocktail evenings. Every afternoon was spent at the RAF Club; school started and finished early because of the heat. While my brother and I would splash about in the pool, Mum would sit with her friends, having a coffee or sometimes something stronger.

For the kids, there were regular movie nights. One of my earliest memories was watching *One Hundred and One Dalmatians*, with the screen on one side of the pool, and us sitting on the other.

Other memories include birthday parties in the garden, with swings and slides; Christmas in the sunshine, with Father Christmas arriving by boat, and the chocolate and strawberry milkshakes at infants' school.

Holidays were spent at Fraser's Hill on the mainland of Malaya, where temperatures were slightly cooler. We had two trips up there that were eventful for very different reasons.

Trip number one involved an overnight stop in Kuala Lumpur. The King of Malaya had recently died, and by sheer luck we were there for the funeral. We had a balcony room overlooking the funeral procession: ringside seats that would have been worth a pretty penny (or Malaysian Cent).

On trip number two we never actually made it to our destination. The family occasionally talked afterward about 'the accident', but not at any great length, and I don't remember it myself – probably a good thing. I was horrified to learn the gory details when my brother was writing his life story.

To quote from my brother Barry's recollection:

> Soon after crossing into Malaya, disaster struck. A car travelling in the opposite direction pulled out too far, causing a head on collision. The next minutes and hours are a blur, but still remain fixed in my mind. I was lying down at the point of impact so missed what actually happened and also escaped any injury. I soon became very distressed for my sister, Valerie, who was covered with blood and appeared seriously injured. Dad was grimacing through

obvious pain in his arm. It later transpired that he had broken his arm, raising it up to stop Valerie going through the windscreen; she had been sitting on his lap on the front passenger seat. Although she had a bad cut to her mouth, she had escaped serious injury. Gordon had a nasty cut on his hand but me, Mum and Barbara all escaped unharmed.

Within minutes, a police Land Rover arrived at the scene, bundled everyone (including the severely injured driver of the other car) into the open back of their vehicle and sped off to hospital. This journey was the most traumatic part of the incident for me. After being involved in an accident, to find myself then in an open vehicle travelling at high speed with frequent swerves down the middle of a busy road and a policeman shouting over and over again, "hospitaaal, hospitaaal" into his walkie-talkie proved quite an ordeal.

A final twist in the story was still to come. Gordon's car was, of course, a write off leaving the family stranded in Malaya, so the police told them to call when they were discharged from hospital and they would give them a lift. Hours later the hospital made a similar offer to take them home in an ambulance. This they declined as they had already accepted the police offer.

True to their word, the police picked everyone up, but at the Malay/Singapore border made the surprise announcement that this was as far as they could go and "dumped" the family at the causeway.

I found this distressing reading and still do. It's quite possible my dad saved my life that day.

After three memorable years in Singapore, we flew back home in July 1962. Mum relates the story that we started our descent in a violent thunderstorm. At the time of the announcement "Please return to your seats", she was stuck in the toilet and couldn't get out due to the turbulence. Every time she tried to open the door, the plane lurched and she was thrown backwards. Eventually, she made her escape and got back to her seat and soon after, we landed on English soil, to miserable grey skies and cold rain.

That following winter was one of the worst in UK history; people called it "The Big Freeze". How we must have missed those glorious Singapore temperatures.

Fast-forward fifty years, and I was fortunate to return, and share with my husband the place where I had spent such happy times. It was an emotional visit. I'd only just lost my dad the year before and he was very much in my thoughts, particularly as we came in to land at

Changi where he had worked. It was a real goose-bump moment, and brought tears to my eyes when the pilot announced, "Welcome to Singapore".

I felt I'd come home.

~~~

The Final Place

Tessa Thomson

She held his hand, she touched his face,
She stared around the peaceful place,
Its whitened walls; its squeaky floor
its smell of death; and so much more.
She didn't know his life before,
Its ups and downs and so much more

She didn't know that he could dance.
His body once left nought to chance
When taking to the floor at night
To give some lucky girl delight.
She didn't know his life before,
Its ups and downs and so much more

She didn't know how hard he worked
A job he loathed but never shirked,
To give his wife and child a home,
From which he prayed they'd never roam.
She didn't know his life before,
Its ups and downs and so much more.

His garden space, his place of life,
His plants, his birds, his paradise.
He tended saplings till they bloomed.
He watched them grow to nature's tune.
She didn't know his life before,
Its ups and downs and so much more.

She didn't see the man of heart,
The lover, husband, man apart.
But hold his heart, and check it now,
Was this what caused the final bow?
She didn't know his life before,
Its ups and downs and so much more.

She looked again to see his face,
Lined and grey but in God's grace.
She couldn't know his younger self,
The richness of his life. Not wealth,
But richness of the proper kind:
Loving family, peace of mind.
She didn't know his life before,
Its ups and downs and so much more.

She saw his body, wasted now,
Frail and spent, but still somehow
A pride laid bare, a man of means.
A gentle soul. A man of dreams.

Some unfulfilled, some left too late
To gather in before his date
With God, his maker and his strength,
His passion gone, his life well spent.

She didn't know his life before
Its ups and downs and so much more.
To her, it's simple cut and thrust:
Find the cause, lay the dust,
Tell the family what she can,
Keep the image of the man
Whose life she didn't know before,
Its ups and downs, and so much more.

~~~

A Sunday Excursion

Wendy Fletcher

In the days of the Sunday Excursion, steam engines from all parts of the country hauled long trains of carriages to the sea every week of the summer. Each would carry full loads of passengers.

We lived a mile and a half from our local station and regularly walked there to board. Father carried our provisions for the day in Mother's shopping bag, and she had our macs draped over her arm.

I skipped along between them, questioning my captive audience, often not even waiting for an answer as new ideas flitted through my mind.

'How come we 'ave a queen but no king? 'Why d'ladies wear bonnits at Easter? 'What birds built them nests?'

As we neared the station buildings, a sign announced Whittlesea, and I always felt that this was where our journey began: an adventure taking us out of our little town – which had been known as Whittlesey for decades – back in time to the days when we were nearer the sea and had been an island in the Fens, back to the world of steam where the spelling of our name had never been corrupted.

We joined the throng of other families queuing at the ticket office before reaching the one platform for eastbound trains, curiously offset so that it wasn't quite opposite the westbound platform. A waiting room with leather benches was always open, with windows looking out towards the track. An imposing fireplace suggested that travellers might huddle by a blazing fire on colder days but I never remember seeing a fire, perhaps because we only ever ventured out in summer.

Outside, there were metal benches and red fire-buckets. The hanging baskets were always well-tended in this era when the rural railways were a credit to those responsible for their upkeep. Uniformed staff were on hand, always looking efficient. They could be relied on for up-to-date information and an informal chat about the prospect of a long hot day, sea breezes and tide times.

There were crowds on the short platform every week, all eagerly awaiting the same train, and the conversation was animated. These were the people of the brickyard community and those who cultivated the land under the unpredictable Fen skies, and they were going to savour every moment of this hard-earned day out.

The men were less likely to wear a suit than in the previous decade. Now it was more common to see them in light trousers and an open-necked shirt, sometimes sporting a blazer for the seaside. Both men and women wore open-toed sandals, the men with socks.

The women had dresses, belted at the waist and buttoned right down to the hem, with a tendency to pop the lowest button if they stretched a leg too far. They all clutched shopping bags or covered baskets, often opened for the first helping of freshly-made white bread sandwiches, before the last of the carriages clattered out of the station.

A cluster of children jigged around them as they waited, thin white legs beneath their shorts, each dangling a bucket and spade. Balls were carried in net bags and an early version of 'flat-pack' was the beach ball, only inflated once it reached the beach where it was considered safe to play. This myth persisted despite the fact that they were regularly caught by the wind and whipped along the sand, outpacing both children and parents, usually finishing up in the surf and bobbing out to sea.

All around me, I saw relaxed faces and laughing children but the knot in my stomach would be getting uncomfortable now. Although I spent my entire childhood living in the familiar surroundings of a pair of 1887, Great Eastern Railway carriages, I had an uneasy relationship with trains that moved.

The first sign of an imminent arrival was the gate-keeper strolling across the road, closing the gates in case an occasional car should come that way. Now all faces turned west, necks craned to get the first glimpse of the puffing smoke in the distance. I held the hands of my parents, clinging tighter as it got nearer, lumbering into the station. The image in my memory is of screeching brakes and steam, hissing and swirling around us as it shuddered to a halt, the power temporarily reigned in, but poised to surge forward again, like a horse only half-tamed. And I was terrified of horses too.

Behind the engine were men with blackened faces who stoked the boilers. Their smiles were probably genuine but I looked away, afraid that I might meet their eyes: white orbs against the soot-covered background. My clearest memories are not of the engine or the carriages, but of the spaces where the couplings met. On one occasion, when I had been brave enough to look down into this ravine, I saw a sheer wall dropping into darkness, a pit of hot vapour reaching up to me with curling fingers. From then on, I didn't even look.

Just moments before this had been an innocuous space beyond the platform where rails glinted in the early morning sun, drawing the eye to the distance where the space between them appeared to narrow. Now it had become a dark chasm into which a small child might slip, impaling herself on the greasy, dripping metal.

But not this child, who was pulling her parents backwards as they tried to move forward with the crowd.

At home, we had concrete steps to each door. I had clambered in and out ever since I learned to walk, suffering only a few minor scrapes when I lost my footing. But here, on these bright Sunday mornings, I faced the nightmare of climbing from the platform to the narrow step, hardly wider than a ledge, and up to the carriage. This was an ordeal to be overcome as quickly as possible if I wanted to see the sea. I just extended one leg and screwed up my eyes, as the parent behind steadied me from falling backwards and the parent in front hauled me to safety. I bet they thanked the Lord they had only one child.

Once inside, I was fine. These trains were designed for comfort and travelling was a pleasant experience. I perched on the edge of the long seats with my feet on the floor or sat back against the upholstery, being unable to do both at the same time. The antimacassars were starched white, and armrests could be lowered or raised. If I kneeled on the seat, I could see my reflection and that of my parents in the bevelled mirrors. Pastel paintings showed relaxing scenes of the countryside and coast, and posters advertised boating holidays on the Norfolk Broads for four pounds. The woodwork had a high sheen, windows were clean and blinds could be pulled down to give shade from the sunlight. Lamps were turned on by individual switches, and a pull-cord, safely out of reach, bore the words, 'in case of emergency'.

Bags were stowed on the luggage racks overhead, and we settled down for the journey. The noise of the engine was muffled to a background sound, and the smoke was just an occasional distraction as it wafted past the window. I enjoyed the rhythm and the rocking motion as we passed signal boxes clad in the traditional tar paper, and clackety-clacked over the points. The vibration of the glass was soothing against my face as I watched the shifting scenery. Like countless other children, I was intrigued by the wires that stretched between the telegraph poles at the side of the track and seemed to rise and fall before my eyes.

I tried to spot rabbits as they scurried into their burrows in banks that rose steeply on both sides. Often, long stretches of grass lay blackened, where it had been set on fire and left charred by sparks from the engine. We saw cows and sheep and horses, so used to the passing trains that they barely paused in their chewing to mark our passage. Men in fields of wheat, searching for tares, straightened their backs slowly, pained by lumbago yet waving cheerfully. Later in summer, bales of hay stood in these same fields awaiting collection, and I always looked for windmills, mostly disused by this time, often sad and derelict and without their sails.

Occasionally we ventured as far as Great Yarmouth, with its reputation as the finest seaside on the east coast, but Mother always thought this was not such good value as the travelling time was longer, lessening the time spent there. Our normal destination was Hunstanton and we got to know this route well, always looking for the same landmarks. One of these was a church that had fallen into disrepair and become overgrown. As Father pointed it out, commenting on its neglected state, a fellow passenger volunteered the information that it was abandoned following a tragic wedding when the bride had collapsed and died at the altar. I have no idea if this was true, or even where the church was, but from that day on, we never passed the spot without experiencing a moment's sadness for that poor woman.

Through the Fens and into Norfolk, we crossed many level crossings although they were never level as shrinkage of the surrounding peat meant a raised hump where the track was higher than the farmland and roads up to the gates were more like hills. We tooted to warn tractors and walkers of our approach, then glided past as they waited below, their passage barred as we commanded right of way. Sometimes, there were children with bikes and I looked down at them, imagining how sad they must feel that they could only go for a bike ride while we sallied forth in a shining carriage.

As we passed through Wolferton, my parents always commented on the regal status of this station, with its coronets of wrought iron and leaded windows. They explained that this was where the royal train stopped to allow the Queen and her family to alight on their journeys to nearby Sandringham House. Now I understood the wistful look of those waiting children, who must surely have imagined that I was a princess, perhaps accompanied by my governess, at the beginning of a long summer retreat. I never once spoiled this vision by asking myself how much they would have laughed if they had seen me earlier, being wrestled into the carriage like an obstinate donkey.

At Snettisham we marvelled at the intricacy of the hedge which was sculpted to include the name of the station and the letters GER. Approaching Heacham we started to see the first signs of holiday accommodation, caravans and chalets, dotted across a wide, flat area reminiscent of the Fens. Another structure we always looked out for in the last minutes of the journey, was an old carriage at the far side of a field, squashed against a hedge. It appeared to have been lifted into the air and dropped there by the wind but Father claimed – and again I don't know if there is any evidence – that it was a relic of the 1953 floods, carried inland to its final resting place by the surge that had devastated this coastline, and left there where the hedge had caught it, stranded as the water receded.

Now that we were getting nearer to the coast, the excitement grew and voices reached a higher pitch. Parents began to retrieve the remnants of picnics and round up their children. I seemed to have less trouble getting out of the train, being able to leap over the gap to whichever parent was waiting to catch me on the platform. Then it was just a matter of cramming as much as possible into the short hours before we had to leave again.

My parents hired stripey, canvas deckchairs by the hour and sat close to the water's edge while I splashed in the surf. They only moved to shuffle the chairs back if the tide threatened to reach their feet or the shopping bag. This was when I most envied those children who had come in a pack of siblings and now chased a ball or ran in and out of the water, kicking up a spray, splashing and squealing to each other. I watched, but was always too shy to join them and eventually Father would be moved to stir from his chair and kick the ball around with me. I know he tried to compensate for my lack of company but it was never quite the same.

I watched the waves, and he skimmed stones out to sea, a skill I never acquired despite his patient endeavours to teach me the wrist movement. He did build me some pretty impressive sand castles and at least I was spared the tears that came from further up the beach: a brother insisting it was an accident when he trod on someone's newly completed masterpiece, a sister protesting her innocence when sand was kicked into another child's eyes. By comparison my play was sedate and my ball never escaped to the freedom of the surf.

At this time, there was still a pier strutting out to sea and a boating lake, as well as a skating rink, fairground rides and indoor amusements. We ate a packed lunch on the sand if it wasn't too windy. On rougher days we found a space in one of the concrete shelters built into the wall that enclosed the boating lake. Here, we unwrapped our food on the slatted benches, often fish paste or cheese sandwiches. It was not until much later that I realised that sandwiches could contain more than one filling. They did not have to be cheese or tomato, fish paste or cucumber. Some people combined these ingredients.

On one occasion, I had mouth ulcers and could only chew very slowly. A chilly wind was blowing into the shelter and Mother, having finished her own food and keen to move on, suggested that I finished eating mine as we walked. I struggled with that dry cheese sandwich all the way from the boating lake to the pier, feeling too poorly to even appreciate the novelty of being allowed to eat as I walked, something she would never have permitted if we had been in our own town where someone might have recognised me.

'Eatin' yer food in th'street. What 'ud folks think?' she would have scolded.

A band played on the Green and shops were always open on Sundays, selling trinkets and souvenirs. I loved the cheap jewellery, the garish ornaments and, as I learned to read, the postcard stand where I liked to join Father, though I was often disappointed as he moved on, drawing my attention elsewhere before I could ask awkward questions about the meaning of double-entendres. Kiosks on the front offered sticks of rock, and ice-cream could be bought from vendors who pedalled along the prom on specially adapted bicycles. I don't remember ever having hot-dogs or burgers, but we ate fish and chips out of newspaper in the late afternoon, or took them to share with my aunt and uncle if they were at their summer residence: a caravan on a site at the end of the fair.

When a refreshing breeze came off the sea, we might walk along the sand as far as Old Hunstanton, famous for its russet and crimson striped cliffs. These were pleasant enough, but I never found them as impressive as the knot-holes, nearer to home, with their jagged, jutting faces. Paths with overhanging flowers led to the formal gardens at the top of these cliffs and, from this high vantage point, we could see right across the Wash to Skegness. On days that were clear of sea mist, it was possible to discern the outline of the tower of St Botolph's church, known locally as 'Boston Stump', as it rose from the flat Fens of Lincolnshire.

One Sunday, the breeze brought in a plague of ladybirds, and the promenade literally crawled with them. We sat at a table on the raised balcony outside the café, just beyond the caravan site, with a pot of tea and had to sweep them aside before we could put down the cups. All around us people were brushing ladybirds out of their hair and picking them from their clothes.

It was amazing to see, but my most vivid memory of these excursion days is of the train pulling out of the station on the return trip, leaving behind the beautiful, orange glow of the sun setting over the sea, a sight not normally seen on the east coast, but possible at Hunstanton because the town actually faces west.

Then it was a sleepy journey home and a slow procession back from the station with parents carrying the smallest children, the slightly bigger ones straggling behind, their exuberance of the morning now spent.

At each turning, families branched off to their own street until we walked alone again, back to the safety of our carriages that didn't move.

~~~

An excerpt from The Railway Carriage Child: *a work in progress*

Fred's Legacy

Cathy Cade

We bought a pre-loved camper-van.
We'd travelled up by train.
The owner's dog had crept inside
and wouldn't come out again.

The lady planned to emigrate.
She'd shown us both around
Watched carefully by Algernon,
an indeterminate hound.

Embarrassed, she said, 'Take him too.
'He won't cost much to feed.
'He can't come when I emigrate.
So... shall I get his lead?'

When Jim and I and Algernon
(with dog bed, lead and trough)
Were halfway down the A1(M),
the camper-van took off!

Jim fought it through the back roads
till it stopped outside a pub.

We all leapt out.
One bystander gave Algie's ears a rub.

He said, 'That's Fred's dog – and his bus!
Fred died in that there 'van.
'Was camped on t'moors.
Two days it were before they found the man.'

Tears in his eyes, he told of Fred
and faithful Algernon.
'He barked and barked till someone came.
Fred's daughter took him on.'

Now, spooked and fearful, off we went,
but Jim mistook the track.
A cloud of starlings formed an arrow
pointing our way back.

The engine gently coughed
as we approached a petrol bay.
Jim hadn't noticed fuel was low.
The next was miles away.

The light was fading when, at home,
I raised my evening drink.
'Thanks, Fred, for looking after us.'
I'll swear, one headlight winked.

~~~

Delivering the News

Philip Cumberland

I was about, or just under, thirteen years old when starting my first paper round in Huntingdon – a morning round, using a Pashley small-front-wheel large-basket trades bike. I added a Sunday round next, in a different part of town. At that time, there was competition for paper rounds, even waiting lists. My evening round was the most interesting. Whereas, with the morning and Sunday rounds I worked for a newsagent, the evening round was my first taste of self-employment.

An older lad leaving school gave me the round. Papers were bought direct from a wholesaler, and sold to the public. In 1964 the gross profit per paper was one penny – the old penny: large and 240 to the pound.

The wholesaler used an office at a garage and taxi company in Ferrar's Road. It was situated in the back corner of a rectangular cobbled yard; the house at the front was the garage owner's. There were workshops down one side of the yard and a high wall opposite. The back of the yard, away from the house, had more buildings and an arch with a driveway underneath, leading to lock-up single garages rented to the public.

The office contained a desk, a typewriter and chair, two largish tables, two more chairs, a telephone, tea-making facilities, and a large machine for printing 'Stop Press' onto the papers. The evening papers sold by my wholesaler were London papers: The Evening News and The Standard. He was also the local wholesaler for a few magazines, one of which was Private Eye: a good read even then.

After finishing school, dropping my things at home, and collecting the trades bike, it was off to the wholesalers. There I collected about a dozen papers before cycling to the railway station. At the station, I sold papers to waiting passengers on the platform nearest the ticket office. Then, crossing the footbridge to the northbound platform, I sold to commuters waiting there. When the express train from London arrived – I can't remember whether, at that point, they were still steam or early diesels – more papers were collected from the guard's carriage. The two bundles were carried back over the bridge – Evening News on my right shoulder, Evening Standards in my left hand – heaved into the basket of my bike, and I would be off.

There was a steepish hill out of the station to George Street, but George Street was thankfully downhill. I used a short-cut down cobbled Royal Oak Passage to the High Street. The passage had a central gutter then with an iron drain about halfway along. One day the bike's front wheel caught in the drain, catapulting me over the handlebars. The bike stood on its end, the heavy papers pinning the basket to the ground.

Once through the passageway, my journey would continue up the High Street to the wholesaler's delivering the papers to the office.

Stop Press news would be received by telephone and transcribed in shorthand by the wholesaler's secretary, who was the garage owner's wife. This news was typed up onto a Roneo stencil, a narrow strip that looked like carbon paper, perforated at one end. The stencil was loaded onto a drum at one end of the Stop Press machine, the papers placed onto a shelf at the other end then fed onto a conveyer by hand. The conveyer belt passed papers under the rotating drum that printed the news updates onto each paper in turn.

Once a dozen papers were printed, I would take them to a nearby factory, The Silent Channel, which made rubber mouldings and guide channels for vehicle windows. I cycled around the factory to sell as many papers as possible before returning to the wholesaler to collect the rest of my papers. The other distributor at the wholesaler had driven off by then in his Austin A30, delivering papers to local newsagents.

Once loaded, I would head for the house of my assistant, Stephen. His was the original round, acquired from my predecessor. Once he had his papers, I was off: next stop French's offices and hostel. This company was building London overspill estates, enlarging Huntingdon. After selling papers around their premises, I delivered my own round, looking out for prospective customers at the same time. A small *John Bull* printing set enabled me to produce advertising cards for evening paper delivery services. I would follow these up with a call, which often gained me new customers.

I gave my business to Stephen when I left school, aged fifteen, but I kept a Sunday round on for a few years afterwards. I still have a Sunday paper round – have had for fifteen years or so, but in a different town.

~~~

Knots and Crises

Cathy Cade

The bicycle was in its usual place. It looked worse in daylight – spokes bent, tyres slashed... I didn't waste time assessing the rest of the damage. I wouldn't mourn the hated thing, but I mourned my easy, queue-free journey to work. At least I could have a few drinks at lunchtime.

At work, I took shelter in the basement, savouring – for the last time – its familiar smell of dust and crumbling bindings. I'd worked in this building since I graduated.

Above ground the lift rumbled shut. It descended, screeching like the banshee, and settled with a groan to open with a waft of spice. Kris blinked out, like a bespectacled hamster, hands gripping the high bar of the trolley. It trundled out and the door sighed shut behind.

We hugged and I flinched.

'Not again, Nicky. Let me see.' Behind the rimless lenses anger flickered.

'It's nothing. Really.'

Pursed lips signalled disbelief but the subject was dropped. 'Work won't be the same without you here.'

My new job would bring a modest salary increase but hardly enough to motivate a move.

Kris frowned at the loaded trolley.

'Why don't I send someone down to put this away?'

'I might as well do something useful,' I said. 'Filing's all I'm good for today.'

Alone, I felt a flutter in my left eyelid, like an insect flexing under the skin. It wasn't visible unless I looked *very* closely in the mirror at the right time. I ignored it and began sorting the trolley.

As the lift reached ground level, my phone rang. Voicemails waited: 'Where *are* you, Nicky? Call me!'

A knot tightened inside my ribcage. The phone rang again.

'I've been calling you all bloody morning! Where've you been?'

'In the basement; there's no signal there. What's the problem?'

'Have you seen my wallet?'

'Why? Can't you find it?'

Alex sighed heavily. 'You haven't tidied it away somewhere?'

'Have you looked in the car?'

'Of course I've looked in the bloody car. I've looked everywhere. Now I'll have to cancel the cards. Damn! All those security questions I can never remember.'

'I could do it at the bank, at lunchtime.'

Alex didn't answer.

'It's nearly lunchtime now.'

Silence.

'Unless you want to look again first.'

'Bugger!'

I waited.

'Get me some cash then while you're there. I need to go shopping. I'll have to come and pick it up – bloody nuisance, losing your licence.'

'How much d'you need? There's Billy's piggy bank.'

'No, I borrowed it... to pay the milkman. Till I get some cash.'

'I emptied my change in it last night – should be nearly ten.' Enough for a half-bottle.

'Oh. Well. Get me a hundred then – tide me over till the new cards come.'

'Fine. I may be–'

Alex had closed the call. I pocketed the phone as Nelson came out of the office.

'Nicky – your last day! End of an era. Are we going to the Hope and Anchor after work?'

'No, lunchtime.' Nelson hadn't been here long. 'I'll be there for both lunch breaks. If they don't like it they can sack me.'

Seasoned colleagues knew I didn't stay after work.

At my desk, I took the wallet from my pocket and emptied it. There was a gym membership card and a progress record for Wing Chun Kung Fu, stamped up to blue belt.

Debit and credit cards went back in my pocket; everything else went in the bin.

At five fifteen, the Department Head looked in on her way out.

'Family all well? Good, Good. Billy must be walking now... how's dog training coming along?'

I blinked. 'I'm afraid we lost Dusty. She got out in the road.'

Dusty had been a rescued terrier cross: a feather duster on legs.

'Oh. That must have been upsetting.'

'It was.'

It had upset me. Billy missed her too.

'Well... I wish you all the best, Nicky. Good. Keep in touch.'

'Of course.'

Kris returned from the washroom. 'Bert wants to know when we're going. They lock up early on Fridays.'

'Did anyone miss me when I left the pub?'

'I said you'd gone for more cash. How was it?'

'As expected. The credit card's cancelled and they've frozen the joint account, but they need both our signatures to take my name off. When Alex signs, I'll clear the overdraft.'

My new bank had already agreed the loan. From my bag, I took a folder with 'Nicky's Stuff' scrawled across it and handed it to Kris, along with the envelope I'd collected from Personnel that afternoon. The Wing Chun card mocked me from the waste bin. I picked it up and turned it over.

'You'll like this... it says a true warrior never picks a fight or loses his temper.'

'Your Alex must have missed that part.'

I tore it up. As I handed over my desk keys, a hint of spice claimed the workspace. My briefcase now held a phone charger and two pens. I dropped in Alex's cash to keep them company.

'Text me first tomorrow,' I said, 'just in case.' My insides flipped; we didn't have a Plan B. 'I shouldn't take long packing. Our clothes are piled in laundry baskets as if they're waiting to be put away.'

'It will be – what do you call it? – sod's law if you get home and find Alex has put them away for you.'

We shared a smile at this unlikely prospect.

I'd loved our ground floor maisonette when we moved in. The bike was still in the front garden, padlocked to the fence. My insides curled. I waved to Billy at the window. He disappeared. I opened the door.

'Where the hell have you been?'

Billy flung his arms around my legs and clung like Velcro.

Alex can seem mouse-like when meeting strangers; neither of us is tall. At home though, it's a different kettle of rodents: fierce, spitting ones.

'The meeting ran over.'

'Meeting? On Friday afternoon?'

Could I have blamed public transport? Best not to mention the bike. The banknotes were accepted without comment. I picked up Billy, who was dry but smelly.

I didn't look at Alex – eye contact could be interpreted as a challenge. Dog training hadn't been a complete waste of time.

'Bicky.' Billy pounded a bruise. 'Bicky, bicky.'

The pasta I'd left for his lunch was still in the fridge so I popped it in the microwave and settled him in his highchair.

'Where was this meeting then – in the pub?'

'Er... yes. Actually... there was a leaving do. I went in to pay for the first round.'

'You could've said so in the first place. How can I trust you, Nicky, when you lie to me all the time?'

More-in-sorrow-than-anger. My eyelid stirred.

I said, 'I'll cook, shall I?'

'I haven't done anything about dinner yet; I've been looking for work – sending emails.'

Reading mine more like; all junk, I hoped. I'd been careful not to log in to the new email account from my laptop.

Spooning pasta into Billy's open mouth, I almost flinched when a hand touched my neck. It took all my self-control not to arch away from the fingers trailing down my spine. I slid sideways, leaving Billy to finish feeding himself.

'I'll go run his bath. Keep an eye on him, Al.'

'He doesn't need a bath every night.'

He wouldn't if he didn't smell of pee, but I didn't say so.

Later, tucking him into bed, it struck me how his baby features had sharpened – pointy and wary. Like my toddler photos. I wished again we had kept him with the childminder after Alex left that last job.

I found his comfort dog, Ussy – well-washed and mended, as was its predecessor before it disappeared. Like Dusty had.

Alex said she must have got out when the man came to read the meter, but Dusty wasn't a dog to wander. A vet had phoned as I was leaving work – not our vet. This one found my number from the microchip register. Somebody came across Dusty lying in the road and took her in to him. He'd had to put her down. When I got home, she wasn't waiting behind the door to greet me.

While I was cooking, an arm snaked around my waist. 'I'll open a bottle of wine shall I? Get us in the mood?'

No. Please, not tonight.

'I'm really tired, love.'

I waited for the explosion but it didn't come. Why not?

I rubbed my eyelid. Had I given something away? Was Alex trying to lower my guard so I'd let something slip? Was I being paranoid?

We'd been going through a bad patch. These days, our marriage was a quilt-load of bad patches, but last night's attack was the worst yet. I'd been powerless to defend myself for fear of leaving scratches, or bruises, or anything to suggest I might be unfit to have Billy.

We'd had truces in the past – even apologies – and Alex always meant them at the time, but tonight felt different. Tonight there was an edge to the overtures.

The wine bottle was almost empty. My knotted stomach didn't want the food. Life with Alex had become a succession of knots.

Only Kris knew how to loosen them until they slithered away, like snakes into grass.

Under the table, a shoeless foot travelled up my inner leg to my thigh. There would be more trouble if I rejected it.

Still, I didn't expect to throw up. The repercussions woke Billy.

In his room, as I bent to comfort him, a bottle flew over my head and bounced off the window blind onto the bed. I picked it up and turned to see Alex, red-faced, coming for me.

I scrambled across the bed and sprinted for the door, flinging Billy's dressing gown at Alex's head. Surprise won me seconds. Dodging into our room next door, I threw the bottle the other way, toward the kitchen. Alex roared out, following the noise, and I slid back into Billy's room. With my knee against the door I gripped the handle to stop it turning, while my free hand groped for the key I'd taped over the lintel. I fumbled it into the lock and turned.

It was a trick that wouldn't work twice.

I rocked Billy until the kicking at the door stopped, and then the knife blows.

And the threats.

'Ussy?'

I found Ussy, and clean pyjamas. Billy's eyes were round and wet. I saw my own childhood in them – praying for the shouts to stop before they turned to punches. As I grew, I'd try to shield my mother and get knocked aside – caught in the crossfire, even when I wasn't the target.

Sharing Billy's narrow bed I curved around him, allowing my thoughts, and my tic, to dance unchecked. Alex had known a troubled childhood too; it had brought us together. We'd shared our stories and planned our perfect family – babies and a dog.

I washed and dressed Billy as soon as he woke. I saw his eyes take in the damage as I whisked him past the bedroom door. We were having breakfast when Alex burst into the kitchen. Last night wasn't mentioned.

'I can't be late. I have to get new membership cards.' The tone suggested this was my fault. 'I'd give blood to know what happened to those cards.'

Whose blood wasn't specified. Suspicion bored into the back of my neck.

I said, 'Will the gym want proof of ID?'

'Oh bugger! They probably will. Where's my driving licence?' Alex scuttled out to the living room. 'It stinks in here!'

I hadn't cleaned up last night; it wasn't a priority now. Drawers slammed. One fell out.

'Damn – I'm going to be late. Now I'm knackered before I start!'

That sounded ominous.

I crossed my fingers. 'Perhaps you should give it a miss today.'

'Oh you'd like that, wouldn't you? It's all right for you – you get to talk to adults all day while I'm stuck here with a screaming kid. The one thing I look forward to all week...'

Billy's face began to crumple. Breathing again, I went to help and found the folder marked 'Alex's Stuff' in an unopened drawer.

'Driving licence or passport?'

Alex snatched the passport and the door slammed. We were alone.

I'd mentally rehearsed this moment.

I sat Billy among his toys, and went to stuff clothes into bin bags.

An incoming text buzzed in my pocket. Kris was outside. I texted back, 'AOK,' and grabbed another bag.

What else?

'Pee-pee.'

Not *now*, Billy. I couldn't ignore him though, like Al did. I left him shuffling around the kitchen on his pot. We would shop later for a new one. I grabbed a feeder mug.

Kris had parked across the road on double yellow lines. I waved and left the bags on the doorstep. How could I have done this alone? I wouldn't get my driving licence back till next year.

That had been the fallout from a neighbour's housewarming. I'd collected Billy from their bedroom and carried him home, and he never woke – until our front door closed behind us and fists started pounding my back.

Apparently I'd spent too long talking to the new neighbour.

I needed to get away, so I grabbed the car keys, and locked us in the car while I fastened Billy's seat straps. Then I drove – away from the shouting and the banging, and the neighbours' windows lighting up.

I parked around the corner.

When police knocked on the window, brandishing a breathalyser, I was behind the wheel with the key in the ignition.

Unlucky?

Billy had shuffled as far as the hallway, where the carpet edge tipped his pot. I left it for Alex and discarded the wet slippers – something else for the shopping list. Socks and shoes would have to wait – they were in a bag.

I'd need the briefcase... and my laptop – it would be good to have that back. What else, what else? I scooped random toys into another bag.

Time!

'Come on, Billy,' I grabbed the buggy.

'No!'

I lifted him, wriggling. The bags were gone from the doorstep; Kris was loading them into the hatchback.

'Ussy!'

Kris came for Billy and nodded toward the battered bike. 'At least it wasn't Billy.'

This time.

I went back in. Ussy was under the high chair – could I take the high chair?

No time.

One last look... I'd loved this place. The door closed behind me.

A traffic warden was writing a parking ticket; the car's owner came running out. Kris was strapping Billy into the toddler seat we fitted yesterday.

I delivered Ussy, stowed the buggy and closed the hatchback... revealing Alex at the end of the street, chatting to an attractive, track-suited woman. At the crossing they laughed and parted.

Alex turned toward home as I ducked into the passenger seat, bent double, as if searching the floor. I tugged the door shut.

'Kris. It's Alex.'

Kris clipped the last strap, closed Billy's door and slipped behind the steering wheel. A suggestion of spice teased my cramped airways as we drove off, with me still inspecting the carpet.

An alarm sounded, and I twisted my neck in panic.

'My car requests that you fasten your seatbelt. We have passed your Alex. She hasn't seen you.'

Appointments jostled in my head. On Monday, Billy was to meet the new childminder and I would go to the clinic to have my knife wound re-dressed. It wasn't deep, but I'd taken it to Accident and Emergency on Thursday night, so I'd have a record of it.

On Tuesday I had an appointment with the solicitor.

On Wednesday I would begin my new job.

My mobile rang. I muted the ringtone.

After a while it stopped vibrating, and then began again. I didn't pick up the voicemail.

A text alert appeared. 'Where R U????'

I removed the SIM card and threw it out of the window. Kris glanced across.

I was looking forward to a shower and change of clothes. It would have to be a hand-held shower to keep the dressing dry...

The bathroom!

I'd forgotten the bathroom. I mentally added toothbrushes to my shopping list, and an electric shaver.

The car hummed as it idled at traffic lights. There was rumoured to be a women's refuge somewhere around her. No men's refuges though.

Billy had fallen asleep clutching Ussy. I sighed, like a balloon deflating, and felt the tic tapping at my eyelid like an old friend.

Knots began to unwind.

~~~

Thoughts from Hell

Tessa Thomson

I thought of you again last night
And wondered how it felt
To live and die and spend such time
In fear and hate and hell.

I called your name, apparently.
I never do most times.
I don't remember, when I wake,
Those thoughts and shouts and cries.

There're locked inside. I feel them most
In pleasure or in pain,
When my heart and body search to know
The cause of all this shame.

Was it me? Did I do something wrong?
Did I bring out in you
Something you feared to show the world
Lest they think less of you?

Did you harm me so I could feel
The hurt you felt inside?

Was all that pain a learning curve,
To make me want to hide?

Don't tell a soul, you said to me.
No one must ever know,
Or all your love I'll never see
And into hell I'll go.

You came so quiet but I always knew.
That scent of cigarettes carried you.
You didn't speak just crept behind,
Touched me, pressed me, left me blind.

I had no-one that I could tell.
No-one whose trust I felt
Could do for me what I deserved,
Be kept a child, not left in hell.

~~~

Princess

Valerie Fish

Daisy had taken her time getting ready that morning, wanting to look her best for the big occasion, although every day for her was a dressing-up day. She couldn't understand the young girls of today who went out half dressed, everything hanging out, not caring how they looked.

Princess had already been to the poodle parlour earlier on, the red bow was her crowning glory. Daisy's matching sweater had been a last minute brainwave.

They'd travelled this route many times before. Princess usually loved it on the top deck, peeking out of her mistress's handbag, staring out of the window, watching the world go by.

Today was different; she sat there still and subdued, not making a sound, not even a whimper. Daisy wondered if she had an inkling as to where she was going.

Daisy sat on the top deck on the way home with an empty handbag, staring out of the window, watching the world go by.

She hadn't cried – 'stiff upper-lip' as papa had taught her. She hadn't thought of mama in a long time but now Daisy wondered, would mama be looking after her Princess?

The thought of them both together opened the floodgates and there, on the top deck of the 223 to Uxbridge, all alone, Daisy wept.

~~~

Tales from St Rodney's

George Holmes

St. Rodney's Church serves a parish containing the affluent southwestern village of Nasty Underhill. Many of the parishioners are retired and some have military backgrounds. Of those that work, many commute to London, to work in professional capacities.

The parish magazine is an interesting and popular publication. Occasionally a Special Edition reprints popular articles from throughout the year. This is the latest.

Mums Can't Tell Mockers from Knockers

In a recent survey conducted for The Fiddle in Hell Rat Strangling Society – president, Sir Willoughby Spam-Hamper (Bart.) – it was established that a large proportion (75%) of the Mums interviewed could not distinguish Mockers from Knockers.

Mavis Sidebottom said it was a sign of the times and thought that the filth on television was to blame.

Gertrude Frisby-Down said that they ought to bring back National Service, and since they had stopped putting real toads in Toad in the Hole, the country had gone to rack and ruin. There was a general call for the resignation of the Archbishop of Canterbury, and one or two ladies even called for him to be flogged.

Mrs. Evadne Strict said she would consider taking the contract for her usual price. Sir Willoughby said he could vouch for her thoroughness.

Letter of Complaint from Dame Evadne Strict

Small ads placed in the parish magazine help with production costs, with any profit donated to local charities. An advertisement offering adult tuition for reluctant learners placed by Mrs. Evadne Strict was printed with an incorrect telephone number – co-incidentally, that of *Dame* Evadne Strict who is a Conservative member of the House of Lords. Dame Evadne lives in a nearby village that shares the same telephone exchange. The fact that she speaks as a junior minister for adult education only added to the confusion. Her letter of complaint is published below.

House of Lords
Westminister

Dear Editor

My local vicar showed me an advertisement in the recent copy of your magazine. He is, I understand, a regular reader.

I should like to make it clear that I, Dame Evadne Strict, am not the Mrs. Evadne Strict mentioned in the advertisement offering adult tuition services.

Furthermore, I do not offer flagellation services to the nobility or, for that matter, to anyone else, either in a professional or any other capacity.

Mrs Strict, no doubt, as an independent woman, must make her own way in the world and earn her living in the way she considers appropriate.

My telephone has been ringing constantly, with gentlemen – and I use that word in its loosest sense possible – making the most outrageous requests. I have had to resort to the answer-phone.

If any of the offending gentlemen are among the readers of this publication, please note the type, colour and state of my underwear is none of their business. Furthermore, it is not for sale.

Some callers were imprudent in not withholding their telephone numbers. These will be contacted by my solicitors (Messrs. Rackman and Fleecing) in due course – in particular, the gentleman whose conversational skills seem limited to panting like an asthmatic red setter into the mouthpiece of the telephone.

I expect to see this letter published in full, together with an apology and correction in your next edition.

Yours sincerely,
Dame Evadne Strict

Nativity at St Rodney's

This year's Nativity play proved very entertaining.

Regular readers will know that Mrs Evadne Strict has recently been appointed treasurer for the Parochial Church Council. In that capacity, she has instituted a vigorous and successful fundraising campaign.

Unfortunately we are unable, for the time being, to publish Mrs. Strict's photographic contribution to the parish magazine – *District Councillors' Unusual Hobbies* – but the PCC would like to thank those gentleman for their generous donations.

So successful was fundraising for the Nativity that a singularly professional production was possible. Mrs. Strict declined the part of the Virgin Mary, which caused hilarity in some quarters. An invitation to join in *While Shepherds Watched their Flocks by Night,* prompted a remark from the floor that they would bloody well need to round here. To forestall further comment, *Hark the Herald Angels* was substituted.

Colonel Braddock-Smythe announced his intention to fire a star shell from his Howitzer, to replicate the Star in the East. (How he managed to hang on to the field gun after leaving the Royal artillery nobody knows.)

Reverend Peter (Parachute) Peters asked him to aim away from the steeple this time as the weather vane hasn't worked properly since last year.

Admiral Aubrey Strobes livened up the proceedings no end by insisting the choir and cast had a double rum ration before the production. He also ensured that most of the audience had the same fortification. Nobody remembers much of the production but every one who attended thought it was the best ever.

You will all be pleased to learn Molly Saunders, the Girl Guide Captain, has recovered from hypothermia, following her impromptu striptease and swim in the duck-pond. Sir Willoughby Spam-Hamper (Bart.) gallantly fished her out and did what he could to restore her circulation whist waiting for the ambulance.

Hang-gliding and the Clergy.

From the Dorset Enquirer, reproduced with permission.

The Right Reverend Peter (Parachute) Peters has been refused planning permission to erect a jumping-off platform for hang-gliding, from the steeple at St Rodney's church, in the village of Nasty Underhill, Dorset.

Planning permission was refused on grounds that it could incite the suicidal to throw themselves off the steeple, causing large craters in the adjoining public car park.

Sir Willoughby Spam-Hamper (Bart.) welcomed the decision saying that churches were the last place for a jump. He declined to comment further when asked about more suitable choices of venue.

Oddly-shaped Vegetables.

Parishioners were pleased to find Reverend Peter (Parachute) Peters back in St Rodney's pulpit after his short spell in hospital – now fully recovered from his unfortunate accident. The sheep has been returned and the firemen have now resumed their duties.

After giving thanks to members of the fire brigade in his sermon, the vicar commented on a recent change of heart in Brussels regarding rules that govern misshapen vegetables. He defended these as God moving in mysterious ways. "Is not the forked carrot one of God's creations? Is its value any less than that of a straight cucumber?"

At that juncture, an insensitive soul pointed out that it depended if you were a sheep or not.

After the laughter subsided, the congregation sang *All Creatures Great and Small*.

Note on concerns for the health of the sheep:
I omitted to mention Reverend Peters's apology, his course of medication, and Sir Willoughby's large donation to the local RSPCA.

An undertaking was given by certain parties not to publish certain photographs of members of the local constabulary, providing the matter was settled amicably. The health or well-being of no further sheep were put at risk, apart from actions of Mr Jones the butcher (by way of normal trade).

On an unrelated note...

Sir Willoughby Spam-Hamper (Bart), in an act of characteristic generosity, compensated the farmer and made a contribution to the Fire-fighters Fund.

At Sir Willoughby's suggestion, Mrs Evadne Strict is to administer physiotherapy to the vicar to allay his recurring stiffness.

~~~

Let's Talk

Tessa Thomson

Let's talk.
Let's see if we still can.
Let's turn the TV down,
And challenge each one's other view.
Let's miss the weatherman.

Let's talk.
Let's use our wordsmith skills.
Let's verbalise all night.
Let's cure the world's worst ills.
Let's hold our values tight.

Let's talk,
Like in our student days.
Let's argue, rant and rave
And passionately hold our views
Midst others' haughty gaze.

Let's talk of love,
Of others' plights in danger, fear or worse.
Let's not regret our own misdeeds;
Life lived can't be rehearsed.

I know I'm talking to myself.
When did we stop this art?
I watch you watch, yours eyes are glazed.
When did we drift apart?

Let's talk to everyone we meet,
To every lonely soul we can.
"Did you say something then, my dear?
"Ah, you want the weatherman!"

~~~

Delivering Christmas

Cathy Cade

'Twas the night before Christmas
when Santa's new elf,
in the vast, silent workshop, sat all by herself.

She'd been fetching and carrying, sent to and fro
making tea, running errands,
the least of the low.

And she'd mucked out the stables,
not noticing that
daft old Rudolph was munching
her new elven hat.

So it was, that when Santa Claus
marshalled the rest,
Emmie failed to pass muster:
improperly dressed.

As the sleigh jingled off
through the wintery skies,
Em recalled seeing oversized, dark dragonflies.

Every day, as she shovelled snow,
cold and downcast,
she'd heard them approach,
and she'd watched them drone past.

Metal mules don't need feeding,
or stalls mucking out.
She envisaged a prototype, drafted it out.

and, because Emmie Elf was a born engineer,
it was ready for testing soon after New Year.

When old Santa awoke
from his post-Christmas nap – around Easter
– he heard an insistent tap-tap.

He threw open his door,
and the drone that was knocking
flew in, to deliver a filled Christmas stocking.

Santa welcomed technology – no luddite, he.
He went over Em's drawings
with thinly-veiled glee.

His eyes were a-twinkle,
his morning smile, gappy.
"Give 'em antlers, to keep the traditionalists happy."

"With a flight deck
"controlling them all from the sleigh.
"We could beta-test next week.
"Perhaps Saturday."

But the older elves muttered,
though younger ones cheered,
and some glitches occurred,
as the doubters had feared.

Busy months hurried past until summer was gone.
Father Christmas pushed Emmie
to move things along.

Till, at last, Santa's sleigh
had its instrumentation.
The elves shuffled out
for a grand demonstration.

Two took off and crash-dived,
and the next flew too high,
while a fourth was attacked
by a passing magpie.

Then a couple collided,
and one hit the wall,
and a few couldn't pull up their stockings at all

While, it's true,
some delivered their load as directed,
more work would be needed before 'twas perfected.

All the younger, brash elven-folk jeered
and they laughed,
while the older ones claimed
the whole idea was daft.

The concept was fantasy,
science fiction, crass...
"Cos you can't replace reindeer,
"and Emmie's a lass."

angry more with themselves
for beginning to dream
of a cushier Christmas
with Emmie's bold scheme.

But Santa smiled kindly
and smothered a chuckle.
"'Twere worth trying, lass."
Then he tightened his buckle;

December was on them.
While Em tweaked her coding,
the others were sorting,
and packing, and loading.

The adverts and streetlamps
and windows of shops
were a-glitter with tinsel
and other yule props,

and newer elves tidied
and swept, and made tea,
in keen anticipation of Christmas-to-be.

~

'Twas the night before Christmas,
when children in bed
had no notion of Santa's sleigh
parked overhead.

The elves filled the skies
on their metal, winged steeds,
with brass antlers to steer them at dizzying speeds.

Old St. Nick and the reindeer
could rest their tired feet
while the elf-guided drones
made their drops in each street.

Then trailing like stardust,
they followed the sleigh,
wishing, peace, health and laughter
to all on their way.

~~~

THE WHITTLESEY WORDSMITHS

.

THE WHITTLESEY WORDSMITHS

We are a U3A Creative Writing Group who meet monthly to share our ideas and support each other as we explore our interest in writing prose and poetry, fact, fiction and fantasy.

(The U3A is an organisation for people no longer in full-time employment. You can find your local UK branch at https://www.u3a.org.uk/.)

Follow our blog at https://whittleseywordsmiths.com or email us at whittleseywordsmiths@gmail.com.

Wendy Fletcher

Wendy grew up in two Great Eastern Railway carriages just outside Whittlesey.

Following a period of living in Norfolk and Suffolk, she returned to Whittlesey in 2009.

She spent the next few years, writing of her childhood experiences in an autobiography called 'The Railway Carriage Child', to be published in the New Year.

Realising what a lonely hobby writing can be, she set up the U3A Creative Writing Group, which has evolved into the Whittlesey Wordsmiths and is still growing.

Jan Cunningham

Jan is a lady of advanced years who always wanted to write fiction but never got round to it. Now with the help of the Whittlesey U3A writing group she is at last realising her dream.

Stephen Oliver: a (very) Short Biography

Stephen is the son of an RAF dental surgeon father and a Swiss mother and spent his childhood moving from place to place.

He spent the greater part of his career as a Software Engineer in Switzerland, working for banks, insurance companies and a nuclear research facility. When he closed his company down in 2012 to return to the UK, he decided to devote his time to writing.

In 2013, he self-published a self-help book titled *Unleash Your Dreams: Going Beyond Goal Setting*, before turning his attention to fiction. Since then, he has started writing a fantasy novel, and has completed three urban fantasy and science fiction short story anthologies, all of them dark or darkly humorous. A fourth collection is already in progress. He is presently looking for a publisher.

An inveterate 'pantser' or discovery writer, Stephen writes his stories on the fly, finding out for himself what they are all about as he types. Although this may seem a chaotic way of working to some, Stephen has found that there are many others out there who work the same way.

He juggles his writing with looking after his mother, who is in her 80s.

Tessa Thomson

Before joining this writing group Tessa had never written anything down although, blessed with a vivid imagination, had been telling stories most of her life. Some have been rather tall tales which have become embellished over time.

Tessa only came to live in the Fens with her husband recently, having spent the last 8 years living in South-West France. Her short stories tend to be on the light side, often romantic, never with a moral. Her poems tend to be darker.

Tessa has found the writing group uplifting and freeing, and the members supportive and kind about her attempts to write. She continues to learn.

Val Chapman

Having won a national essay competition at junior school in the North-East, she decided to quit while she was ahead.

Life then got in the way and, with no prior experience, Val thought she would pop along to her local U3A writing group on a whim, and loved it.

It has taken Val 60 years to start this writing lark. It might take her another 60 to get the hang of it.

Aside from this new-found hobby, Val loves animals, cake, and her family. Sometimes in that order.

Teresa Gilbertson

Teresa is one of life's triers. Not having found her niche she continues to try.

Perhaps that is her forte as people often refer to her as very trying!

Valerie Fish

Valerie's love of the English language dates from her school days, inspired by a fantastic English teacher. Her writing philosophy is 'Less is More', enjoying flash fiction and contributing regularly to online competitions, her favourite being a story written within the confines of a text message.

She is also a limerick lover, and has had several of her witty verses published in the Daily Mail.

Caroline Cowan

Caroline has always enjoyed reading and loves the sound and flow of unusual words. She produced a monthly magazine for one of the sewing factories she worked in, and once wrote a lot of poetry.

After a very long break, she has now started writing again and is really enjoying it, thanks to the U3A Wordsmiths.

Philip Cumberland

Philip is possibly the oldest paperboy in Whittlesey and the Fens (see 'Delivering the News', first published in *Best of British* as 'Read All About It', May 2018).

In many ways that sums him up: he hasn't moved on much in many ways since his teens.

Born in 1951 in Paxton he grew up in Huntingdon, spending his working life involved in the motor trade and engineering, the last thirty years of his working life running a small business.

For years, Philip has been fascinated with improving his art of writing but like many people didn't pursue his dream until later in life. A vivid imagination and the ability to inject humour into his writing are indicative of his youthful mind. More recently, he has penned a variety of short stories featured in this book.

When he puts his pen down, Philip enjoys the fens, music, reading, walking, cycling and being a general nuisance, according to his wife.

George Holmes

George, originally from Lincolnshire, is a guest contributor to this book. Being an intermittent writer, it is fair to say it is some time since he last put pen to paper. Hopefully, we will be able to coax more work from him in the future. He is a renowned but secretive ghostwriter, known only to a few people.

Cathy Cade

Cathy is a retired librarian whose writing was formerly limited to instruction leaflets for students, with only annual reports to exercise her imagination. Since retiring to Fenland, she has been producing a different kind of fiction, writing short stories with a novel in (slow) progress.

Knots and Crises was published in the Spring 2018 edition of *Scribble* magazine, after coming third in their short story competition of the previous autumn. Other writing has been shortlisted in two competitions, longlisted in one, come third in a *Scribble* article competition, and been published in *Best of British* magazine and *To Hull and Back Short Story Anthology 2018*.

Cathy can be found online at www.cathy-cade.com.

~~~

If you have enjoyed our book,

please leave a review on Amazon.

Acknowledgements

This collection of writing is a collaborative venture; everyone in our group has contributed to it.

I am privileged to be among talented writers. All have been courageous in starting or resuming their writing slightly later in life than they should have. Without everyone's efforts, this book would not exist.

Special additional thanks to

...Cathy and Wendy for proof reading;

...Cathy for compiling;

... Stephen for help with technical aspects;

...Wendy for setting up the group, and poking and prodding us along in the right direction.

Thanks too, to you the reader for whom this book was written.

Philip Cumberland, Editor.

PS: Thanks are also due to Phil, whose idea it was to publish this book and who has worked tirelessly to put it together.

Wendy Fletcher